the runner's journal

chart your progress to a fitter faster you

SEAN KEOGH

axis books

the runner's journal

chart your progress to a fitter faster you

axis books

Published in the United Kingdom 2012
by Axis Books Limited
8c Accommodation Road
London NW11 8ED

www.axispublishing.co.uk

Creative Director: Siân Keogh
Designer: Simon de Lotz
Editor: Anna Southgate
Production: Bili Books

ISBN: 978-1-908621-01-6

9 8 7 6 5 4 3 2 1

Printed and bound in China

Contents

how to use this journal **6**

why run? **8**

food for fitness **10**

balancing your diet **12**

refuelling on a run **14**

rules of training **16**

cross-training **18**

basic heart-rate training **20**

speedwork **22**

motivation **24**

dealing with injury **26**

what clothing do I need? **28**

sole mates **30**

beginner schedule **32**

intermediate schedule **34**

advanced schedule **36**

running diary **38**

how to use this book

The more you put into this book, literally, the more you will get out of it. These pages explain how the running diary section of this book will work for you.

Every day of the week is featured in the diary, with space to record the time, session, or race. There is also space for a comment, such as how you felt, and who you ran with. At the end of each week, there is space to note your comments on how your running has gone, and how you felt before and after the run, together with refueling notes: that is, what you ate and drank that made you feel good (or bad). A sugary drink while you

DAILY LOG

For every week there is a daily diary to fill out, for a complete record of what you have achieved in your running and speedwork training.

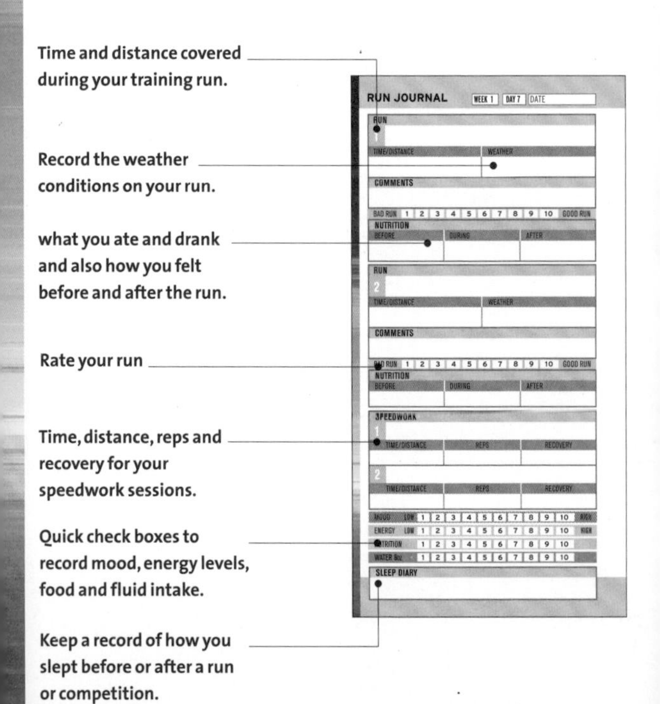

were running, for example, may have given you an extra energy boost, or a high-carb meal too close to your run may have slowed you down. After every four-week period, there is space to record how the month has gone for you. For example, you didn't make it to the club very often, but you did manage to run at lunchtime regularly. Note this down, and you may find a pattern emerges. If there is a problem, you will find it when you look back over your notes.

It's a good idea to fill in the daily log as soon after your session as possible, perhaps over a rehydrating glass of water. That way, you won't forget anything that could be important.

WEEKLY LOG

At the end of each week there is a summary of the last seven days running, recording the goals you have achieved and your general well being for the week. This will help you monitor your progress and allow you to set goals for the next week.

WEEK 5 SUMMARY DATE

GOALS MET

GOALS EXCEEDED

NEXT WEEK

RUNNING NOTES

SPEEDWORK NOTES

REFUELING NOTES

	Calories consumed	
MINUS	Calories Used	
EQUALS	Net Calories	
	BMR	
	net calories deficit	

VITAMINS	DOSAGE	QTY

MOOD
1 2 3 4 5 6 7 8 9 10

ENERGY LEVEL
1 2 3 4 5 6 7 8 9 10

Journal

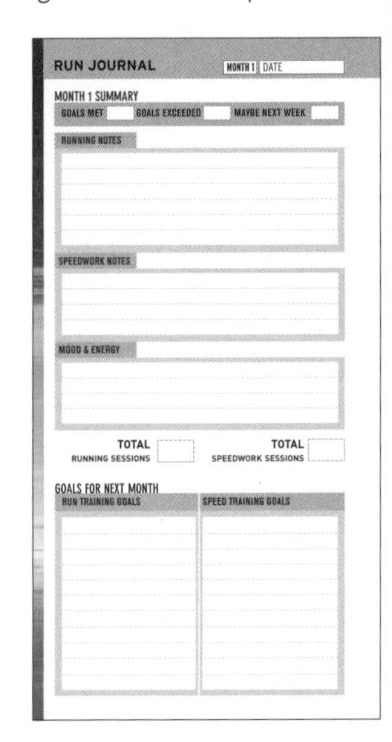

RUN JOURNAL MONTH 1 DATE

MONTH 1 SUMMARY
GOALS MET GOALS EXCEEDED MAYBE NEXT WEEK

RUNNING NOTES

SPEEDWORK NOTES

MOOD & ENERGY

TOTAL RUNNING SESSIONS TOTAL SPEEDWORK SESSIONS

GOALS FOR NEXT MONTH
RUN TRAINING GOALS SPEED TRAINING GOALS

MONTHLY SUMMARY

At the end of each four-week training period, fill out the monthly summary of what has gone well, and not so well, and what you want to achieve in your next month's training. Be careful to set yourself achievable targets.

Why run?

Running can be exactly what you want it to be. There are no rules: you can run by yourself, with one friend or with 10; you can run just to clear your head and unwind at the end of the day; or you can follow a schedule to achieve distances and times you never thought possible. More importantly, it is a free passport to a side of yourself you may never have enjoyed before – a healthier, more relaxed, more confident you. Before starting any exercise routine you should check you are fit and healthy.

ASK YOURSELF THESE QUESTIONS.	
1	Has your doctor ever advised you not to exercise?
2	Have you ever had a heart problem?
3	Do you experience chest pain when you do take exercise?
4	Have you ever had a bone, joint, or muscle injury?
5	Are you taking prescribed medication?
6	Have you ever fainted, lost consciousness, or suffered from dizziness that has caused you to lose your balance?
7	Are you pregnant?
8	Do you have any on-going health concern that may affect your ability to exercise?
9	Do you have a cold or fever, or any other health problem that may make delaying your exercise program wise?
10	Is there any other reason why you should not exercise?

If you have answered 'yes' to one or more of these questions, it is vital to seek the advice of your doctor before you embark on a training programme.

THE BENEFITS OF RUNNING

WEIGHT LOSS

Running burns calories faster than any other activity. One mile of running uses 100 calories; just a 30-minute run can burn 250–500 calories.

QUIET TIME

Forget about your to-do list for 40 minutes – simply breathe fresh air and enjoy being alone with (or without) your thoughts.

BETTER HEALTH

Running boosts your body's immunity to illness. Run for 145 minutes a week, for example, and you will be 40 percent less likely to suffer a heart attack. It improves your blood cholesterol level, and it fights diabetes, arthritis, and osteoporosis.

MORE ENERGY/BETTER BODY

Exercising will help your body work more efficiently, with improved metabolism and cell regeneration. Your body's lean-to-fat ratio will improve, and your calves, thighs, hips, and buttocks will become stronger and shapelier.

LESS STRESS

Runners are less prone to depression than sedentary people. This is partly because of the endorphins that the body releases but also because they enjoy the benefits of achieving new goals and targets.

HEALTHIER LIFESTYLE

Running will make you think about your lifestyle. You will very probably adopt better sleeping habits and give up smoking and heavy drinking. Many runners also prefer to eat healthier foods.

CONFIDENCE

You will feel better because you know that you are fit and motivated and achieving your running goals. This will inspire you in other areas of life.

A KNOWLEDGE OF YOUR BODY

You will discover what kinds of effort your body responds to best. If you race or do speedwork, you will find out how your body reacts to pressure.

food for fitness

Fueling your body properly will not only help you to realize the full benefits of your training program, but also to live a healthier, more energized life.

Eating is a pleasure, and we want to keep it that way. With a few basic guiding principles, your diet can provide you with all the necessary fuel and building blocks for an active, rewarding lifestyle. You will run well, look great, and you certainly won't need to go through hell to get there. We show you how to construct a balanced diet to eat and drink effectively when you are a regular runner. Take a look at these five main food groups.

FOOD GROUPS

carbohydrate

Carbohydrate is essentially energy food. There are two main types of carbohydrate – simple (sugars) and complex (mostly starches) – and you need a balance of both to be healthy. The glycemic index (G.I.) of a food, not just whether it contains simple or complex carbohydrates, determines the speed at which energy is released into the body. Foods with a high glycemic index (which give a rapid rise in blood sugar) include bread and potatoes, as well as bananas, raisins, and sugars such as glucose. Moderate glycemic index foods include pasta, noodles, oats, oranges, and sponge cakes; and low glycemic index foods include apples, figs, plums, beans, dairy products, and fructose. Low G.I. foods raise your energy levels slowly, and therefore give you energy for longer. You need to eat a variety of G.I. foods.

fruit and vegetables

Fresh fruit and vegetables are nutritional powerhouses. If you eat at least five portions a day you will meet the body's quota for vitamins A and C, and gain potassium, fibre, and carbohydrate. Dark-green, leafy vegetables include plenty of iron, which benefits the blood. Broccoli, spinach, peppers, tomatoes, and carrots are particularly beneficial foods.

protein

Protein helps your body to build and maintain muscles, tendons, and fibres. The most obvious sources are meat and fish (which also contain the highest number of essential amino acids). Vegetable proteins are important too, and peas, beans, nuts, lentils, and seeds can provide your daily requirement. You need two servings of protein a day.

WEIGHT CONTROL

If you want a guaranteed weight-loss plan, try this: exercise more and eat more healthfully. This is easier said than done, but nearly everyone who takes up running loses weight. Also, eating healthy food does not mean eating less, it just means eating thoughtfully.

TAKE A REALISTIC LOOK AT WHAT YOU EAT

One way to avoid bad eating habits is to plan your day's eating in advance. Take healthy snacks such as bagels and dried fruit to work in order to avoid the vending machine.

fats

Fat is essential for proper cellular functioning, for the protection of internal organs, and for carrying the fat-soluble vitamins A, D, E, and K. Most of us eat more than enough fat, but if you severely restrict your intake, you risk harming your body.

milk and dairy products

Dairy foods help to keep your bones strong, because they are high in calcium, and they also contain protein and riboflavin, which is used in metabolism. All runners need calcium, but especially women under 20 or above 50, who should aim for four servings a day. One serving equates to a small carton of low-fat yogurt, three slices of cheese, or a small glass of milk. Canned fish such as sardines also contain calcium.

MAKE SMALL CHANGES

Change your diet gradually – turn to low-fat milk instead of whole milk, and replace one or two red-meat meals a week with vegetarian alternatives.

EAT LITTLE AND OFTEN

Healthy snacking (or "grazing") throughout the day burns more calories and keeps your body better fueled than eating big meals.

RUN MORE

Every mile you run uses around 100 calories, no matter at what speed. Build up slowly, and if you are already running at your safe limit, consider adding another activity to your routine, such as cycling, swimming, or a weights session in the gym or at home.

RUN HARDER

Increasing the intensity of your runs burns more calories. Once you have become a regular runner, incorporate speedwork, hillwork, or threshold runs into your routine.

balancing your diet

A runner's body needs a combination of carbohydrate, protein and fat to keep it energized and healthy. The chart below gives you the correct balance and examples of ideal foodstuffs.

The percentages on this chart relate to calories, not weight. This is very important, because one ounce of fat contains more than twice the calories of one ounce of carbohydrate or protein. It is simple, really – burn more calories than you eat, and you will lose weight.

YOU NEED

CARBOHYDRATE

60–70 percent. Approximately 0.1 oz per lb of body weight per day (4–6 g per kg).

SO EAT: Pasta, rice, potatoes, oats, bananas, raisins, figs, plums

PROTEIN

15 percent. Approximately 0.03 oz per lb of body weight per day (1.0–1.5 g per kg).

SO EAT: Meat, fish or seafood, dairy products, nuts, peas, beans and lentils

FAT

15–25 percent (40 percent monounsaturated, 40 percent polyunsaturated, 20 percent saturated) Approximately 0.02 oz per lb of body weight per day (0.4–1.1 g per kg).

SO EAT: Fats, oils, butter, peanuts, avocados and dairy products, such as whole milk and yogurt

Why can't we be more specific about the number of ounces of carbohydrate, protein, and fat the body needs each day?
Because your daily calorie requirement depends on many factors, including your metabolism, your exercise levels and your gender, as well as your weight. (see "Your Calorie Needs," far right)

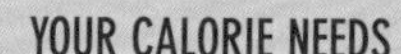

YOUR CALORIE NEEDS

You can calculate your approximate daily calorie needs like this:

BASAL METABOLIC RATE

These are the number of calories your body uses at rest:

Men:
11 calories per lb of body weight (**24** calories per kg)

Women:
10 calories per lb of body weight (**22** calories per kg)

LIFESTYLE

Add **30–40** percent for a sedentary occupation.
Add **50–60** percent for an active occupation.

EXERCISE

Add 100 calories every mile you run.

THE TOTAL

For example, a man weighing **150** lb (**68** kg) would have a basal metabolic rate of approximately:

1,650 calories (**11 x 150**)

He would add **30** percent for a very sedentary occupation (**495** calories), and **500** calories for five daily miles. That gives him a daily calorie need of roughly: **2,645** calories

These figures are guidelines – your basal metabolic rate and the efficiency with which your body extracts calories from food are very individual factors.

refuelling on a run

Vital to any run of more than one hour is maintaining high glycogen and water levels. Without these essential fuels you will very quickly tire and dehydrate.

EATING

When you run, your body takes its energy from easily accessible muscle glycogen (stored, processed carbohydrate), and less accessible fat reserves. We all have fat reserves, but we need to ensure that our glycogen levels are high before, during, and after our runs. That is where smart eating comes in.

BEFORE A RUN

Some people can run within 30 minutes of snacking; others have to forego food for hours to exercise comfortably. Pre-run eating isn't essential on runs of less than an hour, but is for long outings. A little readily available energy makes a difference – a bagel and a glass of fruit juice works well for most people. Remember to avoid too much fat and protein, as they are hard to digest.

DURING A RUN

It can be worth refueling with energy on runs longer than 45 minutes, and between repetitions in short, intense speedwork sessions. Keeping your stomach comfortable is essential, so avoid solid foods, except perhaps easy-to-digest favourites such as sports bars and jelly beans. Consider using sports drinks or gels.

AFTER A RUN

Eating 30–60 minutes after a run will help to minimize stiffness and soreness, especially after a hard effort. Research has shown that the best recipe for muscle recovery is fluid, plus a carbohydrate meal incorporating slightly less than 30 percent protein. You can buy special recovery drinks and bars, although a bowl of cereal with low-fat milk and a banana is a good homemade alternative.

DRINKING

The body needs water for almost all of its functions, including energy release and temperature control – and yet; when we under-drink we wonder why we find training and racing really hard work. Even on inactive days, you should try to drink at least eight glasses of water. You need more when you run. In hot conditions, your body can lose almost four pints through sweat in an hour, which is enough to significantly impair performance.

BEFORE A RUN

You should be well hydrated before you run. This does not mean grabbing a cup of water just beforehand; rather, you should sip little and often throughout the day, and especially the afternoon and evening before a long morning run or a race. Aim to drink half a litre (roughly a pint) half an hour before you train.

DURING A RUN

You won't normally need to drink on runs of less than an hour, but on hot days it can be dangerous not to rehydrate more regularly. Sip little and often rather than gulping. On long runs, a safe rule is to take one small cup of liquid for every 15–20 minutes.

AFTER A RUN

To restore its fluid balance, you will need twice as much water as you lose through sweat. Make a habit of drinking more than normal for two or three hours after you run, and stick to water or a sports drinks containing sodium and low levels of carbohydrate. Weighing yourself before and after a run will show precisely the amount of liquid you have lost: 1lb equals 1pint (1kg equals 1 liter). You will know when you are properly hydrated because your urine will be pale.

rules of training

Follow the four basic training principles below ('golden rules')and you should be well on the way to being a happy, successful runner, whether or not you are following a training schedule.

Every run has a purpose. You may only have 20 minutes to run in your lunch break, or you may want a long run (see box right). If your body demands a recovery day, run at a conversational pace. That will leave you fully recovered and eager for your next session. Conversely, when you do speedwork, you should end the session feeling that you have put in a genuinely tiring effort.

Read the four golden rules, below, and remember that respect for your body is paramount.With these principles under your belt, you will be set for a lifetime of effective and supremely satisfying running.

training sessions

The schedules in this book include a broad range of training sessions – some self-explanatory, some not so obvious. Variety is essential, to keep yourself motivated, and especially to help boost your strength and endurance, the key ingredients to successful long distance running. Here are the main types of sessions (see right).

THE FOUR GOLDEN RULES

BUILD UP SLOWLY

You will avoid injury and improve more quickly in the long term by being patient about increasing your speed and mileage. Increase your weekly mileage by no more than three or four miles a week – less if you are a beginner. Ease gradually into speedwork, once you have built a base of low-intensity running. And avoid increasing speed and mileage at the same time.

TAKE REST DAYS

Your body needs time to recover – in fact it builds its fitness after, rather than during your runs – so you should follow any day of fast or long running with a day of easy running or rest.

TRAINING SESSIONS

BRISK OR THRESHOLD RUNS

Brisk runs equate to approximately half-marathon pace for experienced runners. Usually lasting from 20–40 minutes, which may be broken down into fast and slow segments, they are good for teaching your body to run for longer periods at speed.

SPEEDWORK OR INTERVALS

Fast repetitions interspersed with rest periods – for example, 4 x 800 m with two-minute recoveries. They improve strength, speed, and form, and you don't have to be a "fast" runner to do them!

LONG, SLOW RUNS

The key to building endurance, these are best done on the weekend or on a day off from work. Slow runs might progress to between one and three hours, depending on your goals. Time spent running is more important than speed.

HILL SESSIONS

Speedwork on a slope, with a greater emphasis on power. You run hard uphill, jog down, and repeat. Distance and gradient variations are endless – a typical session would be 8–12 x 1 minute on a steep climb.

FARTLEK

This is Swedish for "speed play" (see page 23), and is a free-form type of speedwork, in which you speed up at random intervals during a normal run.

3

WARM UP AND COOL DOWN

Your muscles, joints, ligaments, and tendons need time to ease into any run, because when you begin they will be short and tight. You should end any run with an easy jog and stretching to relax your muscles.

4

PAY ATTENTION TO INJURY

Damage to your body will only get worse if you try to run through it. If you have persistent pain, rest and put ice on the sore area in the short-term, then seek a diagnosis from your local doctor, a specialist, or a good coach, and make every effort to rehabilitate the injury. Early treatment will bring a swifter recovery.

cross-training

Supplementing your running with other aerobic activities is an excellent way of boosting your fitness with minimal injury risk. Strength and flexibility training – such as weight training and yoga – also have great value.

As well as helping with your general fitness, all other aerobic exercise (such as swimming, cycling, and rowing) should also contribute to making you a stronger runner. Some coaches argue that the way to run better is to run more, but most runners would benefit from adding one or two good-quality cross-training sessions a week. You can use cross-training to replace one easy run a week, although there are definitely some running sessions – such as speedwork and long, slow runs – that cannot be adequately replicated through other activities.

TEN BEST WAYS TO AVOID INJURY

1. **Don't stretch cold muscles**
2. **Wear good running shoes**
3. **Return from illness or injury cautiously**
4. **Cross-train and strength train**
5. **Don't run hard days consecutively**
6. **Build mileage and speed gradually**

Don't ignore pain

Treat pain promptly

Ease into your runs

Run on soft surfaces

get in the pool

Swimming is an excellent way of toning up just about every part of your body as well as giving yourself a good cardiovascular workout. It is also a good way of learning to regulate your breathing.

CROSS-TRAINING TO OVERCOME INJURY

HAMSTRING PULL

ROWING

Some gentle rowing sessions will extend the legs and gently stretch the damaged area. Over time, adding power strengthens the hamstring against future injury.

ACHILLES TENDINITIS

CYCLING

Outdoor cycling or a spin class provides excellent exercise as it stretches and strengthens your Achilles tendons without impacting or twisting.

ELLIPTICAL TRAINER

This is great for injury rehabilitation, as it involves no impact. Elliptical trainers allow you to run in a continuous motion that is a cross between cross-country skiing and stair climbing.

RUNNER'S KNEE

BRISK WALKING

Going for a walk straightens the leg, while exercising with a bent knee (as in cycling) can worsen the problem. Rowing and using an elliptical trainer can also help.

SHINSPLINTS

CYCLING

Shinsplints can be eased through cycling, as it avoids putting pressure on the front of the lower leg. You can also try Nordic skiing and using an elliptical trainer.

PLANTAR FASCILITIS

CYCLING

Pedaling a bike can help to ease the tension on the underside of the foot, although it might be a little painful at first. You can also try rowing and using an elliptical trainer.

basic heart-rate training

A heart-rate monitor can help to ensure that you do not work too hard – or take it too easy! – in training sessions.

Depending on the training session you do your target heart rate will be between 60 percent and 95 percent of your normal working range (see box right). This calculation can only provide an estimate of your maximum heart rate. The more accurate way is to find your maximum through running. Warm up, then run at a fast even pace for three minutes. Rest with two minutes of gentle running, then repeat your three-minute maximal run. During your second run you should get a higher maximum heart rate than with any other method. Use your heart-rate monitor to take readings throughout, as your heart rate may peak before the run is completed. As you get fitter you will need to recalculate this to make sure that you continue to train in the correct heart rate zone to get the most effective workout for your fitness goal.

TRAINING AT THE RIGHT RATE

There are three broad training zones:

60–75 percent	EASY
75–85 percent	MODERATE
85–95 percent	HARD

BUT... DO NOT FALL VICTIM TO A COMMON MISCONCEPTION:

These are not percentages of your overall maximum heart rate; they are percentages based on your working heart rate. It makes a big practical difference to a regular runner.

The calculation is easy to do, but it takes more explanation than most gyms are prepared to give.

FIND YOUR TRAINING ZONE:

Calculate your maximum heart rate (above right), for example, 190 beats per minute (bpm).

Calculate your resting heart rate. This should be done lying still, soon after you wake up. For example, this might be 56 bpm.

Subtract the resting rate from the maximum. This figure is your working heart rate.
For example: 190–56 = 134 bpm

Take the percentage of your working heart rate that you are aiming for – for example, 60 percent for an easy run is 134 x 0.60 = 80 – and add it to your resting heart rate (80+56 = 136). The final figure is your personal target heart rate for the session.

CALCULATE YOUR RATE

To know your target heart rate, you will need to know your maximum. If you are more than 20 percent overweight or a beginner, use the formula right to estimate your maximum:

214 – (0.8 x age) for men
209 – (0.9 x age) for women

For example, a 30 year old man might have a rate of:
0.8 x 30 = 24
214 - 24 =190bpm

SAMPLE SESSIONS

60 PERCENT	Recovery run – dead slow. Although slow, recovery runs are crucial. Takes 30 minutes.
60 to 70 PERCENT	Long, slow run – up to 65 percent the body is teaching itself to burn fat as fuel (useful for marathons). Takes anything from one to three hours.
75 to 85 PERCENT	Fartlek – speed play (moderate-paced runs with random fast bursts). Takes 30–60 minutes. Undulating route – peak at 85 percent on the climbs. Takes 30–90 minutes.
85 PERCENT	Anaerobic threshold run (or 'tempo run'). Approximately ten-mile (16 km) to half-marathon race pace. Sample session: 1.5 miles at 60 percent, then 15–20 minutes at 85 percent, then 1.5 miles at 60 percent.
85 to 90 PERCENT	Approximately 5K to 10K pace. Sample sessions: 6 x 800 m peaking at 90 percent in each repetition; or 5 x 2000 m peaking at 85 percent in each repetition.
95 PERCENT	Peak heart rate at 400 m interval pace (not full-out race pace). Sample session: 12 x 400 m with 200 m jog recoveries, making sure recovery heart rate drops to at least 70 percent.

speedwork

Speedwork (also known as 'intervals' or 'repetitions') is the single best way to become a stronger, faster, more confident runner. A weekly session will pay dividends whether you are a twelve-minute miler or an advanced five-minute miler.

Once you have progressed to running 30–40 minutes or more, three or four times a week, you can think about turning one of your sessions into speedwork. This will be hard work, but you will see the benefits within days: your fitness levels will increase rapidly, and your normal running will become easier and more enjoyable.

types of speedwork

All speedwork includes periods of hard running interspersed with rest. Beyond that, the variations are infinite. You can do speedwork on a measured track or stretch of grass, though exact distances are not essential. The rest interval (during which you stand, jog, or walk) can vary according to the purpose of the session – short

SPEEDWORK SESSIONS

REPETITIONS AND INTERVALS

Sessions of hard running at 5K pace or faster, generally between 200m and 1200m in length, or 30 seconds and five minutes. Include short recovery periods of 30-90 seconds, or the same time or distance as the repetitions.

Running at faster than your race pace for short periods improves your speed, and also helps you to work on your running form. When you push hard, it is important to concentrate on your posture, stride length, and also your arm and hand movement.

TEMPO INTERVALS

Longer than ordinary intervals, tempo intervals take between 90 seconds and 10 minutes, or between 400m and two miles. They are run at slightly slower than your 5K pace. These sessions help to raise the point at which lactic acid builds up in your muscles.

distances and/or long rests are best for building pure speed, while longer distances and/or shorter rests will build speed and endurance. A good rule is to rest for the amount of time it took to run the effort.

Typical sessions might be

8 x 400 m; 4 x 800 m; 3 x 1200 m; or
200 m, 400 m, 800 m, 1200 m, 800 m, 400 m, 200 m (this is called a pyramid session). You can also run by time rather than distance – for example, 8 x 90 seconds, or 4 x 4 minutes.

how hard should you run?

As long as you are making a greater effort than your normal training pace, you are doing speedwork. Once you are used to this style of training, you should be aiming to run hard but evenly – your last repetition in a session should be as strong as your first.

As well as improving your fitness enormously, speedwork also teaches you the valuable art of pacing yourself.

FARTLEK

Swedish for "speed play" this is the enjoyable part of speedwork. It is best done off-road, on grass or trails, and you simply mix bursts of hard running with periods of easy running. Run fast between any two points, such as trees when you feel like it, and as fast as you like.

Fartlek is perfect for runners new to speedwork, as it helps you get used to the sensation of running fast.

HILLWORK

The simplest of speedwork, find a hill that takes between 30 seconds and five minutes to run up at 85-90 percent effort. Jogging back down is the recovery interval.

This is great training for helping you tackle hills during a race.

motivation

Sometimes there are days when we would rather do anything other than go running. This will help you to get out and run.

People give up when they become disappointed. And people get disappointed when their expectations differ from reality. That's why realistic goals are essential. If you are 47 and you have been running seriously for 20 years, don't try to beat your all-time best this year, but aim to beat the age-graded equivalent. And if you are a new runner, do not earmark a marathon as your first running target.

goals, now and later

Everyone needs a combination of long- and short-term aspirations to keep them on the move. The long-term targets give you a general direction; the short-term ones provide regular rewards and act as progress markers. Long-term goals are basically your underlying reasons for running. These could range from getting fit and losing weight to wanting to run a marathon. Your short-term goals should be more specific, such as losing five pounds in four weeks, or preparing for a 10K race. A realistic long-term goal might be to enter next year's marathon, or lose 20 lbs in weight, as well as markedly improve your general health, fitness, and sense of well-being.

motivation for the beginner

BEST WAYS FOR STAYING MOTIVATED

1	RUN FREE-FORM FOR A WEEK Just head out at whatever pace and for however long your body wants to each day.
2	...OR QUIT FOR A WEEK! Especially effective if you are a regular runner. Soon you will be itching to train again.
3	FIND A RUNNING PARTNER Running with a regular partner will encourage you to stick to a routine.
4	KEEP IT VARIED Variety is the spice of life, try a bit of cross-training (see 18–19).

When you are new to running keep in mind all the positive aspects of what running is doing for you. Your aerobic fitness will improve dramatically, you will shed surplus fat, and your body will firm up. As you progress, you will feel better all day as a result of being fit, and your sense of well-being will improve. These may appear exaggerated boasts, but the experience of thousands of runners shows that running really does improve your health. When it is cold and wet outside and you shrink from the idea of running, just remind yourself of the benefits.

BANISH NEGATIVE THOUGHTS

Running is fantastic for the spirit: it is just you, your body, and your thoughts. The trouble begins when you start to believe that you are having a bad run. Here is how to squash those negative thoughts fast:

I'm slower than usual... Sometimes we have heavy, slow, breathless days – or weeks – for no apparent reason. When this happens, make the most of your run, at whatever pace feels right, and don't let a short period define the kind of runner you are. Your performances over a full month provide a better snapshot of your fitness.

This run is going to take forever... Break your runs down into sections – maybe 10-minute chunks, or laps of your local park. On the run, just focus on completing one section at a time (this is also a good mental trick for races). You will be surprised by how fast time passes.

5	BUY NEW SHOES This will help you to feel a renewed sense of purpose in your running.
6	JOIN A CLUB Being encouraged or providing encouragement is a perfect enthusiasm-booster.
7	SET A GOAL Setting yourself an achievable target will help to focus you, keep you motivated and help you to maintain your training schedule.
8	REVIEW YOUR CHART Read your training log and see how much you have achieved.

dealing with injury

Top-level runners know how to push through discomfort. They are also smart enough to pull up at the first sign of pain, as this indicates potential injury.

Unlike discomfort, harmful pain tends to be localized and unfamiliar. If you suffer pain from leg, knee, or foot during or after a run, use our guide (see right) to diagnose the problem or illness.

self-treatment

When pain occurs on a run, stop, stretch lightly, then walk. If the pain then disappears, try a light jog, and then ease back into your run – otherwise cut your run short and return home at once. Once there, apply the RICE treatment (see below), which is effective first aid for most pains and sprains. Do not attempt to diagnose your own injury, and if the pain continues for more than two days, seek medical care – ideally, from a sports medicine specialist, physiotherapist, or osteopath.

TREAT INJURIES WITH RICE:

R–REST

Minimize movement and weight-bearing to the injured area. A couple of days off is an effective cure for many minor injuries. If you feel recovered, swim or walk before resuming running training

C–COMPRESSION

A lightly elasticized bandage will help to reduce swelling further – but do not tie it so tightly that it restricts your circulation.

I–ICE

This reduces the damage from the swelling that accompanies strains and tears. Wrap an ice pack (or a bag of frozen peas) in a damp cloth and apply it to the site of your injury for 15 minutes every hour, or as often as you can during the day. Taking anti-inflammatory drugs such as ibuprofen also helps.

E–ELEVATION

Keeping your leg raised will reduce blood circulation, which in the early stages of an injury will help to limit tissue damage.

A QUICK GUIDE TO FIVE COMMON INJURIES

1 ACHILLES PAIN

CAUSE Pain in your achilles tendons is often caused by an excessive increase in speed or mileage, worn-out shoes, or by overpronation, (see page 30).

TREATMENT Ice and rest are the correct responses; when the swelling has gone, gently start to stretch the lower calf and ankle, massage the affected area.

2 HAMSTRING PAIN

CAUSE Hamstring pains are often caused by a sudden or excessive increase in speed or mileage.

TREATMENT Rest, easy running, and massage are the best solutions to most hamstring tears. Avoid hill running and speedwork, ice the injury, and stretch regularly.

3 KNEE PAIN

CAUSE Knee pain can be caused by a problem with the knee itself, or by a problem elsewhere. Check that muscle tightness isn't the source.

TREATMENT Stretch your outer thigh muscles, gluteal muscles and quads, and mobilize your lower back. Ensure that your shoes provide enough stability for your needs.

4 SHINSPLINTS

CAUSE This pain along the front of the shins is caused by swelling of the muscles, tendons, or bone coverings. It is caused by overpronation (see page 30), increased speed, and running on hard surfaces.

TREATMENT The RICE treatment will help. It is important to stretch and strengthen the shins, ankles, and calves. Avoid running on hard surfaces.

5 PLANTAR FASCILITIS

CAUSE Damage to the thick band that connects your heel to the base of your toes appears as pain at the base of your heel.

TREATMENT Stretch your calves and Achilles tendons. Also curl your toes and shift your weight to the outside of your foot as you stretch. A sports medicine specialist can help with massage and ultrasound treatment.

what clothing do I need?

You can run in an old cotton T-shirt and shorts, as long as they are loose-fitting – but specialized running clothes are more comfortable, and may make you feel inclined to run more frequently.

BASIC SUMMER CLOTHING

For most running, you will need light, cool clothing that does not restrict you. Most runners find that a T-shirt and shorts are enough. Items made from synthetic fibres, such as polyester, are better; they are lighter and warmer than cotton when wet, and many are specially designed to move sweat away from the skin so they feel drier.

RUNNING SHORTS

Running shorts have a light outer layer (usually with a side split for freedom of movement) and a built-in brief. You may want to wear lycra shorts under your running shorts if your legs are prone to chafing.

TECHNICAL SOCKS

These use wicking fibres to keep your feet dry. Look for a snug fit, and consider a wool and nylon mix for wet conditions, as it stays warm and comfortable when damp.

SPORTS BRA

This is a must for women (regardless of bust size). Normal bras reduce breast movement by around 35 percent, but a good sports bra achieves closer to 60 percent.

RUNNING TIGHTS

On cool summer evenings, you might prefer to wear a lightweight pair of full-length running tights or pants. These are usually made from lycra and are very comfortable.

WATER BOTTLE

If you are training for more than 30 minutes, you should increase your fluid levels as you run. Carriers include bike-style water bottles carried on a bottle belt, and hand-held bottles – be careful that the larger ones don't unbalance your running style.

WICKING VEST

Many runners like to wear a sleeveless wicking vest or T-shirt. Wicking vests move sweat from the skin to the outer surface of the fabric, where it evaporates, keeping the body cool.

USE THE LAYERING PRINCIPLE

Wear two or more thin layers in preference to one thick one; this gives you the versatility of being able to add or remove a layer as your body temperature changes. Most runners often find a long-sleeved wicking top and a lightweight jacket to be a successful combination.

BASIC WINTER CLOTHING

For winter running, your clothing needs to be lightweight but protective. A lightweight running jacket, running pants and a long-sleeved thermal top are essential. A vest is less restrictive and very useful in milder weather. Avoid cotton, it gets wet and stays wet, making you uncomfortable. Cotton also draws valuable heat from your skin, good in summer but not in winter.

LIGHTWEIGHT JACKET

Runners produce a lot of sweat, so a lightweight, breathable jacket that lets perspiration escape is a comfortable option. A jacket that breathes well will not only be showerproof, but it will also be wind-resistant, which helps to stave off a chill. Most runners avoid fully waterproof jackets because they cause the body to become hot and sweaty.

WATERPROOF SUIT

Some runners like to train with the protection of a lightweight, fully waterproof jacket and overpants, even if they can cause them to sweat a little.

REFLECTIVE GEAR

On dark nights, you need to be clearly visible. You can buy a reflective vest cheaply. Many shoes, jackets and pants carry reflective patterns.

THERMAL TOP

Also known as a 'base layer', this is a synthetic, long-sleeved T-shirt woven to trap warm air within it. You wear a base layer next to your skin, either by itself on mild days, or under another layer in poor weather. For comfort, a close fit is best.

RUNNING PANTS

A pair of close-fitting running tights, or slightly looser running pants with ankle stirrups, are lighter and faster-drying than cotton sweat pants. Tights tend to be warmest.

GILET

These light windproof and showerproof jackets have legions of running fans. They keep the core of your body warm, leaving your arms unrestricted and your torso well ventilated.

sole mates

Finding the right pair of running shoes can take some time, but it always pays off.

For most runners, a broad forefoot (to allow room for your toes) and a narrow rearfoot (to keep your heel and ankle snugly in place) make a good combination in a shoe. You will need roughly a thumb's width between your big toe and the end of the shoe to keep blisters at bay – many people find they need running shoes that are a size larger than their normal shoe size. Try different brands to compare the fit. Only buy from the internet when replacing a well-trusted pair.

a shoe for your needs

A good all-around shoe combines cushioning (to lessen the impact on your joints and tissues) and stability (to keep your body aligned correctly). The amount of stability you need depends on your gait – that is, the movement of your foot as it goes through the cycle of hitting the ground and pushing off from the toes. If your feet roll inward too much ('overpronate'), you need added stability. If your feet do not roll inward as much as they should ('underpronate', or 'supinate'), you need plenty of cushioning to encourage movement. If your feet are normal (or 'neutral'), you can choose a shoe that lies somewhere in between. A good shop assistant or a biomechanics expert can help to analyse your gait.

A FEW TIPS ON FINDING THE RIGHT SHOE

COST

Cost is not an indication of quality. There are some good shoes at low prices, especially if you have no stability problems or you are a low-mileage runner.

TEST

Test the shoes before buying them to make sure they are right for you. Some stores provide a treadmill or allow you to jog around inside (or if dry, outside) the store.

DESIGN

Do not buy general sports shoes. Specialist running shoes are designed to meet the demands of running and are a must if you want to be comfortable.

WEIGHT

A light shoe may seem ideal, but it can be a fast route to injury, as it may not provide the cushioning and stability you need for everyday training.

WHICH RUNNING SHOE DO I NEED?

PERFORMANCE

These are fast-paced shoes with less cushioning and support than everyday shoes. Used by lighter, quicker runners for brisk training, or by normal runners for racing and speedwork. They usually weigh between 10–11.5 oz (280–320 g) for a UK size 8.

CUSHIONED

Straightforward shoes for runners with no biomechanical problems, or for people with inflexible feet. Often the lightest and softest category. Note that all running shoes are cushioned, not just this particular kind.

MOTION CONTROL

These are heavy-duty shoes for runners whose feet don't roll inward as much as they should ('underpronate'), and for heavier runners who need maximum support.

STABILITY

Shoes with some added stability features, for runners whose feet tend to roll inward a little too much ('overpronate'). For many, they provide an ideal blend of cushioning, smoothness and support.

RACING

These are minimalist shoes with very low weight and maximum responsiveness. They are designed for light, efficient runners, and some are only suitable for short distances. They typically weigh between 7.5–9 oz (200–260 g).

OFF-ROAD 'TRAIL'

'Trail' shoes have added grip for soft or muddy conditions. Only a few types work really well. Studded fell-running shoes are a more extreme version. They are light, with limited cushioning and support, but extraordinary traction.

beginner schedule

The aim of this schedule is to build you up to running 30 minutes nonstop. Once you complete this level you can think of yourself as a 'real' runner, and if you want to, you could enter a 5k race.

WEEK 1

Run 2 minutes, walk 2 minutes.
Do this seven times per session.

WEEK 2

Run 4 minutes, walk 2 minutes.
Do this five times per session.

WEEK 3

Run 6 minutes, walk 2 minutes.
Do this four times per session.

WEEK 3 – HOW'S IT GOING?

Are you running at a conversational pace? Are you feeling ready to run again after the walk breaks? Are you staying free of aches and pains? Yes? Good – you're ready to progress to Week 4. If you answered "no" to any of these questions, repeat the first three weeks schedule. However, if by running at a conversational pace you are finding the runs supremely unchallenging, and your body is free of aches and pains, move on to Week 6.

WEEK 4

Run 8 minutes, walk 2 minutes.
Do this three times per session.

WEEK 5

Run 6 minutes, walk 2 minutes, run 10 minutes,
walk 2 minutes, run 10 minutes, walk 2 minutes

WEEK 6

Run 10 minutes, walk 1 minute.
Do this three times per session.

WEEK 6 – HOW'S IT GOING?

If you are finding it a struggle to get to the end of a 10-minute run, do not worry – just drop down to Week 5, or even Week 4, until your body tells you it is ready to progress further. If you are finding this too easy, skip Week 7, but progress normally through Weeks 8, 9, and 10. Patience is essential to build your running fitness sensibly and to avoid the risk of injury.

WEEK 7

Run 13 minutes, walk 1 minute, run 14 minutes, walk 1 minute.

WEEK 8

Run 15 minutes, walk 1 minute, run 16 minutes, walk 1 minute.

WEEK 9

Run 17 minutes, walk 1 minute, run 18 minutes, walk 1 minute.

WEEK 9 – HOW'S IT GOING?

By now you might be itching to get on to Week 10 and progress through the final longer runs to your 30-minute target. If you are not suffering any aches and pains, and you have cruised easily through the last week's runs, then you should be fine to do just that. If you are not quite so confident, but you do feel ready to start Week 10, feel free to spread the week's five sessions over two weeks instead, alternating each session with easy run/walk days.

WEEK 10

DAY 1: Run 9 minutes, walk 1 minute, run 21 minutes.

DAY 2: Run 7 minutes, walk 1 minute, run 23 minutes.

DAY 3: Run 5 minutes, walk 1 minute, run 25 minutes.

DAY 4: Run 3 minutes, walk 1 minute, run 27 minutes.

DAY 5: Run 30 minutes!

WANT TO PROGRESS FASTER THROUGH THE SCHEDULES?

As long as your body remains completely pain free and you can continue to run at a conversational pace, you can miss every third week in the schedule. Alternatively, run four days a week taking alternate days from an easier and a harder week (for example, Weeks 2 and 3), then move up to alternate days from more difficult weeks (for example, Weeks 4 and 5).

intermediate schedule

Before you begin this level you should be able to run 30 minutes nonstop, three days a week.

WEEK	MONDAY	TUESDAY	WEDNESDAY
1	rest	10 mins jog; then 4 x 2 mins (or 400 m) fast, with 2-min jog recoveries; then 10 mins jog	rest or 25–35 mins slow
CYCLE 2		ADD ONE REPETITION	
2	rest	10 mins slow, then 20 mins fartlek, 10 mins slow	rest or 25–35 mins slow
CYCLE 2		ADD 5 MINS FARTLEK	
3	rest	10 mins slow; 1min, 2 mins, 4 mins, 2 mins, 1 min (or 200 m, 400 m, 800 m, 400 m, 200 m) fast, with equal time recoveries; then 10 mins slow	rest or 30–40 mins slow
CYCLE 2		ADD 30 SECS TO EACH	
4	rest	10 mins slow; then 3 x 4 mins (or 800 m) brisk, with 4-min jog recoveries	rest or 30–40 mins slow
CYCLE 2		ADD 1 MIN TO EACH	

SPEEDWORK GUIDE

Your speedwork pace should be one that you can maintain strongly but evenly. You can expect to be capable of averaging the following times:

IF YOU CAN RUN

60 minutes for 10K

400 m = 2:05

800 m = 4:20

1200 m = 7:10

HOW TO USE THE PROGRAM

First follow the main sessions. If you want to progress when you have comfortably completed the first four-week cycle, repeat the schedule and variations with cycle 2. If you suffer any aches and pains, do not hesitate to replace a long or hard run with a shorter or easier one.

THURSDAY	FRIDAY	SATURDAY	SUNDAY
25–35 mins slow	rest	25–35 mins slow	35–45 mins slow
ADD 5 MINS			ADD 10 MINS
25–35 mins slow	rest	25–35 mins slow	40–50 mins slow
ADD 5 MINS			ADD 15 MINS
25–35 mins slow	rest	25–35 mins slow	45–55 mins slow
ADD 5 MINS			ADD 15 MINS
10 mins slow, then 15-25 mins fartlek	rest	25–35 mins slow	50–60 mins slow
ADD 5 MINS			ADD 15 MINS

IF YOU CAN RUN

55 minutes for 10K
400 m = 1:55
800 m = 4:00
1200 m = 6:35

IF YOU CAN RUN

50 minutes for 10K
400 m = 1:45
800 m = 3:40
1200 m = 6:00

advanced schedule

This level is for those who can run for 25–35 miles (40–56 km) over four to six days a week. It will take you to 10K and half-marathon fitness.

WEEK	MONDAY	TUESDAY	WEDNESDAY
1	rest or 4–5 miles slow	1.5 miles jog; then 6 x 400 m, with 2-min recoveries; 1.5 miles jog	4–5 miles slow
2	rest or 4–5 miles slow	1.5 miles jog; then 6 x 600 m, with 2.5-min recoveries; then 1.5 miles jog	4–5 miles slow
3	rest or 4–5 miles slow	1.5 miles jog; then 1 miles measured time-trial; then 1.5 miles jog	4–5 miles slow
4	rest or 4–5 miles slow	2 miles jog; then 2 x 200 m, 400 m, 800 m, 400 m, 200 m, with recoveries half as long, with extra 3 mins between sets; then 2 miles jog	4–5 miles slow
5	rest or 4–5 miles slow	1.5 miles jog; then 6 x 800 m, with 3-min recoveries; then 1.5 miles jog	5–6 miles slow
6	rest or 4–5 miles slow	1.5 miles jog; then 5 x 1200 m, with 3-min recoveries; then 1.5 miles jog	5–6 miles slow

YOUR GOAL

If you follow this schedule, you can aim for a:
40–50 min 10K; and a 1:30–1:50 half-marathon

TRAINING FOR A 10-MILE RACE

This schedule is a good basis for 10-mile training. However, as well as decreasing the long runs by two or three miles, you can adapt the half-marathon schedules for a 10-mile race by running threshold sessions. For example: Jog a 2-mile warm-up, then run 3–4 miles at 15–20 seconds per mile slower than your 10K speed, then jog a mile to cool down.

THURSDAY	FRIDAY	SATURDAY	SUNDAY
5–6 miles steady	rest	10 mins slow, 15 mins brisk, 10 mins slow	6 miles slow
5–6 miles steady	rest	10 mins slow, then 35 mins fartlek	7 miles slow
5–6 miles steady	rest	1.5 miles jog; then 5 x 800 m, with 3-min recoveries; then 1.5 miles jog	8 miles slow
5–6 miles steady	rest	10 mins slow, 25–30 mins brisk, 10 mins slow	6 miles slow
6–7 miles steady	rest	10 mins slow, then 40 mins fartlek	8 miles slow
7–8 miles steady	rest	2 miles jog; then 12 x 1-min steep hill climbs, jog down; 2 miles jog	9 miles slow

Alternatively, as a long weekend or midweek run, run easy for 2 miles, then at 10-mile pace for 2 miles, then easy for 3 miles, then at 10-mile pace for 2 miles, then easy for a mile. This will get you used to both 10-mile pace and distance.

running diary

One of the keys to enjoying running and making progress is to follow a schedule. This means giving yourself goals to aim for, and a working framework to achieve them. Whether you choose to follow one of the schedules in this book, or one of your own, you can use the running diary to record your daily achievements. Note down the date, time, and duration of each run and how you felt after it.

Additionally, weekly and monthly pages allow you to summarise your training sessions, so you can look back at what you have achieved. There is space to record what worked for you, and what didn't, helping you to plan your training in the future. You can see if a pattern emerges. Use it also to log race distances and the times you achieve.

RUN JOURNAL

WEEK 1 | DAY 1 | DATE

RUN 1

TIME/DISTANCE	WEATHER

COMMENTS

BAD RUN 1 2 3 4 5 6 7 8 9 10 GOOD RUN

NUTRITION

BEFORE	DURING	AFTER

RUN 2

TIME/DISTANCE	WEATHER

COMMENTS

BAD RUN 1 2 3 4 5 6 7 8 9 10 GOOD RUN

NUTRITION

BEFORE	DURING	AFTER

SPEEDWORK

1

TIME/DISTANCE	REPS	RECOVERY

2

TIME/DISTANCE	REPS	RECOVERY

MOOD	LOW	1	2	3	4	5	6	7	8	9	10	HIGH
ENERGY	LOW	1	2	3	4	5	6	7	8	9	10	HIGH
NUTRITION		1	2	3	4	5	6	7	8	9	10	
WATER 8oz		1	2	3	4	5	6	7	8	9	10	

SLEEP DIARY

WEEK 1 | DAY 2 | DATE

RUN 1

TIME/DISTANCE	WEATHER

COMMENTS

BAD RUN 1 2 3 4 5 6 7 8 9 10 GOOD RUN

NUTRITION

BEFORE	DURING	AFTER

RUN 2

TIME/DISTANCE	WEATHER

COMMENTS

BAD RUN 1 2 3 4 5 6 7 8 9 10 GOOD RUN

NUTRITION

BEFORE	DURING	AFTER

SPEEDWORK

1

TIME/DISTANCE	REPS	RECOVERY

2

TIME/DISTANCE	REPS	RECOVERY

MOOD	LOW	1	2	3	4	5	6	7	8	9	10	HIGH
ENERGY	LOW	1	2	3	4	5	6	7	8	9	10	HIGH
NUTRITION		1	2	3	4	5	6	7	8	9	10	
WATER 8oz		1	2	3	4	5	6	7	8	9	10	

SLEEP DIARY

RUN JOURNAL

WEEK 1 | DAY 3 | DATE

RUN 1

TIME/DISTANCE	WEATHER

COMMENTS

BAD RUN 1 2 3 4 5 6 7 8 9 10 GOOD RUN

NUTRITION

BEFORE	DURING	AFTER

RUN 2

TIME/DISTANCE	WEATHER

COMMENTS

BAD RUN 1 2 3 4 5 6 7 8 9 10 GOOD RUN

NUTRITION

BEFORE	DURING	AFTER

SPEEDWORK

1

TIME/DISTANCE	REPS	RECOVERY

2

TIME/DISTANCE	REPS	RECOVERY

MOOD	LOW	1	2	3	4	5	6	7	8	9	10	HIGH
ENERGY	LOW	1	2	3	4	5	6	7	8	9	10	HIGH
NUTRITION		1	2	3	4	5	6	7	8	9	10	
WATER 8oz		1	2	3	4	5	6	7	8	9	10	

SLEEP DIARY

WEEK 1 | DAY 4 | DATE

RUN 1

TIME/DISTANCE	WEATHER

COMMENTS

BAD RUN 1 2 3 4 5 6 7 8 9 10 GOOD RUN

NUTRITION

BEFORE	DURING	AFTER

RUN 2

TIME/DISTANCE	WEATHER

COMMENTS

BAD RUN 1 2 3 4 5 6 7 8 9 10 GOOD RUN

NUTRITION

BEFORE	DURING	AFTER

SPEEDWORK

1

TIME/DISTANCE	REPS	RECOVERY

2

TIME/DISTANCE	REPS	RECOVERY

MOOD	LOW	1	2	3	4	5	6	7	8	9	10	HIGH
ENERGY	LOW	1	2	3	4	5	6	7	8	9	10	HIGH
NUTRITION		1	2	3	4	5	6	7	8	9	10	
WATER 8oz		1	2	3	4	5	6	7	8	9	10	

SLEEP DIARY

RUN JOURNAL

WEEK 1 | DAY 5 | DATE

RUN 1

TIME/DISTANCE	WEATHER

COMMENTS

BAD RUN 1 2 3 4 5 6 7 8 9 10 GOOD RUN

NUTRITION

BEFORE	DURING	AFTER

RUN 2

TIME/DISTANCE	WEATHER

COMMENTS

BAD RUN 1 2 3 4 5 6 7 8 9 10 GOOD RUN

NUTRITION

BEFORE	DURING	AFTER

SPEEDWORK

1

TIME/DISTANCE	REPS	RECOVERY

2

TIME/DISTANCE	REPS	RECOVERY

MOOD	LOW	1	2	3	4	5	6	7	8	9	10	HIGH
ENERGY	LOW	1	2	3	4	5	6	7	8	9	10	HIGH
NUTRITION		1	2	3	4	5	6	7	8	9	10	
WATER 8oz		1	2	3	4	5	6	7	8	9	10	

SLEEP DIARY

WEEK 1	DAY 6	DATE

RUN 1

TIME/DISTANCE	WEATHER

COMMENTS

BAD RUN 1 2 3 4 5 6 7 8 9 10 GOOD RUN

NUTRITION

BEFORE	DURING	AFTER

RUN 2

TIME/DISTANCE	WEATHER

COMMENTS

BAD RUN 1 2 3 4 5 6 7 8 9 10 GOOD RUN

NUTRITION

BEFORE	DURING	AFTER

SPEEDWORK

1

TIME/DISTANCE	REPS	RECOVERY

2

TIME/DISTANCE	REPS	RECOVERY

MOOD	LOW	1	2	3	4	5	6	7	8	9	10	HIGH
ENERGY	LOW	1	2	3	4	5	6	7	8	9	10	HIGH
NUTRITION		1	2	3	4	5	6	7	8	9	10	
WATER 8oz		1	2	3	4	5	6	7	8	9	10	

SLEEP DIARY

RUN JOURNAL

WEEK 1 | DAY 7 | DATE

RUN 1

TIME/DISTANCE	WEATHER

COMMENTS

BAD RUN	1	2	3	4	5	6	7	8	9	10	GOOD RUN

NUTRITION

BEFORE	DURING	AFTER

RUN 2

TIME/DISTANCE	WEATHER

COMMENTS

BAD RUN	1	2	3	4	5	6	7	8	9	10	GOOD RUN

NUTRITION

BEFORE	DURING	AFTER

SPEEDWORK

1

TIME/DISTANCE	REPS	RECOVERY

2

TIME/DISTANCE	REPS	RECOVERY

MOOD	LOW	1	2	3	4	5	6	7	8	9	10	HIGH
ENERGY	LOW	1	2	3	4	5	6	7	8	9	10	HIGH
NUTRITION		1	2	3	4	5	6	7	8	9	10	
WATER 8oz		1	2	3	4	5	6	7	8	9	10	

SLEEP DIARY

WEEK 1 SUMMARY

DATE

GOALS MET

GOALS EXCEEDED

NEXT WEEK

RUNNING NOTES

SPEEDWORK NOTES

REFUELING NOTES

	Calories consumed	
MINUS	Calories Used	
EQUALS	Net Calories	
	BMR	
	net calories deficit	

VITAMINS	DOSAGE	QTY

MOOD

1 2 3 4 5 6 7 8 9 10

ENERGY LEVEL

1 2 3 4 5 6 7 8 9 10

Journal

RUN JOURNAL

WEEK 2 | DAY 1 | DATE

RUN

1

TIME/DISTANCE	WEATHER

COMMENTS

BAD RUN 1 2 3 4 5 6 7 8 9 10 GOOD RUN

NUTRITION

BEFORE	DURING	AFTER

RUN

2

TIME/DISTANCE	WEATHER

COMMENTS

BAD RUN 1 2 3 4 5 6 7 8 9 10 GOOD RUN

NUTRITION

BEFORE	DURING	AFTER

SPEEDWORK

1

TIME/DISTANCE	REPS	RECOVERY

2

TIME/DISTANCE	REPS	RECOVERY

MOOD	LOW	1	2	3	4	5	6	7	8	9	10	HIGH
ENERGY	LOW	1	2	3	4	5	6	7	8	9	10	HIGH
NUTRITION		1	2	3	4	5	6	7	8	9	10	
WATER 8oz		1	2	3	4	5	6	7	8	9	10	

SLEEP DIARY

WEEK 2 | DAY 2 | DATE

RUN 1

TIME/DISTANCE	WEATHER

COMMENTS

BAD RUN 1 2 3 4 5 6 7 8 9 10 GOOD RUN

NUTRITION

BEFORE	DURING	AFTER

RUN 2

TIME/DISTANCE	WEATHER

COMMENTS

BAD RUN 1 2 3 4 5 6 7 8 9 10 GOOD RUN

NUTRITION

BEFORE	DURING	AFTER

SPEEDWORK

1

TIME/DISTANCE	REPS	RECOVERY

2

TIME/DISTANCE	REPS	RECOVERY

MOOD	LOW	1	2	3	4	5	6	7	8	9	10	HIGH
ENERGY	LOW	1	2	3	4	5	6	7	8	9	10	HIGH
NUTRITION		1	2	3	4	5	6	7	8	9	10	
WATER 8oz		1	2	3	4	5	6	7	8	9	10	

SLEEP DIARY

RUN JOURNAL

WEEK 2 | DAY 3 | DATE

RUN

1

TIME/DISTANCE	WEATHER

COMMENTS

BAD RUN 1 2 3 4 5 6 7 8 9 10 GOOD RUN

NUTRITION

BEFORE	DURING	AFTER

RUN

2

TIME/DISTANCE	WEATHER

COMMENTS

BAD RUN 1 2 3 4 5 6 7 8 9 10 GOOD RUN

NUTRITION

BEFORE	DURING	AFTER

SPEEDWORK

1

TIME/DISTANCE	REPS	RECOVERY

2

TIME/DISTANCE	REPS	RECOVERY

MOOD	LOW	1	2	3	4	5	6	7	8	9	10	HIGH
ENERGY	LOW	1	2	3	4	5	6	7	8	9	10	HIGH
NUTRITION		1	2	3	4	5	6	7	8	9	10	
WATER 8oz		1	2	3	4	5	6	7	8	9	10	

SLEEP DIARY

WEEK 2 | DAY 4 | DATE

RUN 1

TIME/DISTANCE	WEATHER

COMMENTS

BAD RUN 1 2 3 4 5 6 7 8 9 10 GOOD RUN

NUTRITION

BEFORE	DURING	AFTER

RUN 2

TIME/DISTANCE	WEATHER

COMMENTS

BAD RUN 1 2 3 4 5 6 7 8 9 10 GOOD RUN

NUTRITION

BEFORE	DURING	AFTER

SPEEDWORK

1

TIME/DISTANCE	REPS	RECOVERY

2

TIME/DISTANCE	REPS	RECOVERY

MOOD	LOW	1	2	3	4	5	6	7	8	9	10	HIGH
ENERGY	LOW	1	2	3	4	5	6	7	8	9	10	HIGH
NUTRITION		1	2	3	4	5	6	7	8	9	10	
WATER 8oz		1	2	3	4	5	6	7	8	9	10	

SLEEP DIARY

RUN JOURNAL

WEEK 2 | DAY 5 | DATE

RUN

1

TIME/DISTANCE	WEATHER

COMMENTS

BAD RUN 1 2 3 4 5 6 7 8 9 10 GOOD RUN

NUTRITION

BEFORE	DURING	AFTER

RUN

2

TIME/DISTANCE	WEATHER

COMMENTS

BAD RUN 1 2 3 4 5 6 7 8 9 10 GOOD RUN

NUTRITION

BEFORE	DURING	AFTER

SPEEDWORK

1

TIME/DISTANCE	REPS	RECOVERY

2

TIME/DISTANCE	REPS	RECOVERY

MOOD	LOW	1	2	3	4	5	6	7	8	9	10	HIGH
ENERGY	LOW	1	2	3	4	5	6	7	8	9	10	HIGH
NUTRITION		1	2	3	4	5	6	7	8	9	10	
WATER 8oz		1	2	3	4	5	6	7	8	9	10	

SLEEP DIARY

WEEK 2 | DAY 6 | DATE

RUN 1

TIME/DISTANCE	WEATHER

COMMENTS

BAD RUN 1 2 3 4 5 6 7 8 9 10 GOOD RUN

NUTRITION

BEFORE	DURING	AFTER

RUN 2

TIME/DISTANCE	WEATHER

COMMENTS

BAD RUN 1 2 3 4 5 6 7 8 9 10 GOOD RUN

NUTRITION

BEFORE	DURING	AFTER

SPEEDWORK

1

TIME/DISTANCE	REPS	RECOVERY

2

TIME/DISTANCE	REPS	RECOVERY

MOOD	LOW	1	2	3	4	5	6	7	8	9	10	HIGH
ENERGY	LOW	1	2	3	4	5	6	7	8	9	10	HIGH
NUTRITION		1	2	3	4	5	6	7	8	9	10	
WATER 8oz		1	2	3	4	5	6	7	8	9	10	

SLEEP DIARY

RUN JOURNAL

WEEK 2 | DAY 7 | DATE

RUN 1

TIME/DISTANCE	WEATHER

COMMENTS

BAD RUN 1 2 3 4 5 6 7 8 9 10 GOOD RUN

NUTRITION

BEFORE	DURING	AFTER

RUN 2

TIME/DISTANCE	WEATHER

COMMENTS

BAD RUN 1 2 3 4 5 6 7 8 9 10 GOOD RUN

NUTRITION

BEFORE	DURING	AFTER

SPEEDWORK

1

TIME/DISTANCE	REPS	RECOVERY

2

TIME/DISTANCE	REPS	RECOVERY

MOOD	LOW	1	2	3	4	5	6	7	8	9	10	HIGH
ENERGY	LOW	1	2	3	4	5	6	7	8	9	10	HIGH
NUTRITION		1	2	3	4	5	6	7	8	9	10	
WATER 8oz		1	2	3	4	5	6	7	8	9	10	

SLEEP DIARY

WEEK 2 SUMMARY

DATE

GOALS MET

GOALS EXCEEDED

NEXT WEEK

RUNNING NOTES

SPEEDWORK NOTES

REFUELING NOTES

	Calories consumed	
MINUS	Calories Used	
EQUALS	Net Calories	
	BMR	
	net calories deficit	

VITAMINS	DOSAGE	QTY

MOOD

1 2 3 4 5 6 7 8 9 10

ENERGY LEVEL

1 2 3 4 5 6 7 8 9 10

Journal

RUN JOURNAL

WEEK 3 | DAY 1 | DATE

RUN 1

TIME/DISTANCE	WEATHER

COMMENTS

BAD RUN 1 2 3 4 5 6 7 8 9 10 GOOD RUN

NUTRITION

BEFORE	DURING	AFTER

RUN 2

TIME/DISTANCE	WEATHER

COMMENTS

BAD RUN 1 2 3 4 5 6 7 8 9 10 GOOD RUN

NUTRITION

BEFORE	DURING	AFTER

SPEEDWORK

1

TIME/DISTANCE	REPS	RECOVERY

2

TIME/DISTANCE	REPS	RECOVERY

MOOD	LOW	1	2	3	4	5	6	7	8	9	10	HIGH
ENERGY	LOW	1	2	3	4	5	6	7	8	9	10	HIGH
NUTRITION		1	2	3	4	5	6	7	8	9	10	
WATER 8oz		1	2	3	4	5	6	7	8	9	10	

SLEEP DIARY

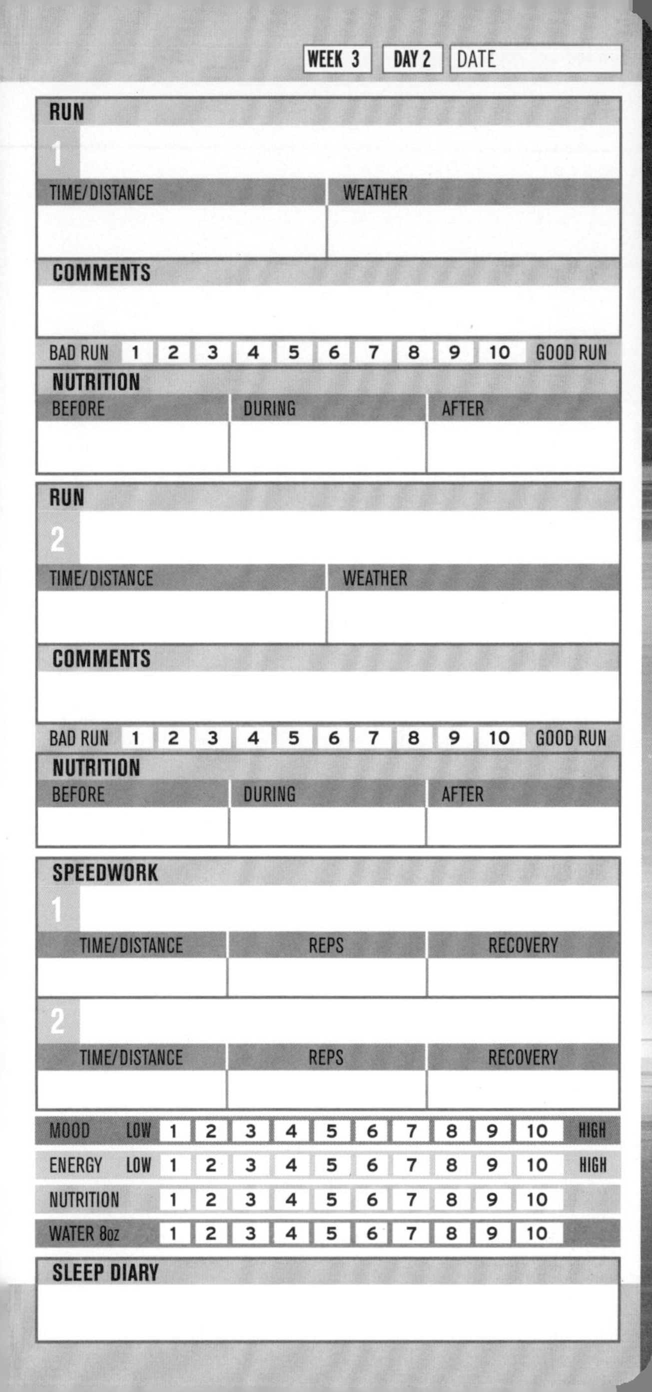

WEEK 3 | DAY 2 | DATE

RUN 1

TIME/DISTANCE	WEATHER

COMMENTS

BAD RUN 1 2 3 4 5 6 7 8 9 10 GOOD RUN

NUTRITION

BEFORE	DURING	AFTER

RUN 2

TIME/DISTANCE	WEATHER

COMMENTS

BAD RUN 1 2 3 4 5 6 7 8 9 10 GOOD RUN

NUTRITION

BEFORE	DURING	AFTER

SPEEDWORK

1

TIME/DISTANCE	REPS	RECOVERY

2

TIME/DISTANCE	REPS	RECOVERY

MOOD	LOW	1	2	3	4	5	6	7	8	9	10	HIGH
ENERGY	LOW	1	2	3	4	5	6	7	8	9	10	HIGH
NUTRITION		1	2	3	4	5	6	7	8	9	10	
WATER 8oz		1	2	3	4	5	6	7	8	9	10	

SLEEP DIARY

RUN JOURNAL

WEEK 3 | DAY 3 | DATE

RUN 1

TIME/DISTANCE	WEATHER

COMMENTS

BAD RUN 1 2 3 4 5 6 7 8 9 10 GOOD RUN

NUTRITION

BEFORE	DURING	AFTER

RUN 2

TIME/DISTANCE	WEATHER

COMMENTS

BAD RUN 1 2 3 4 5 6 7 8 9 10 GOOD RUN

NUTRITION

BEFORE	DURING	AFTER

SPEEDWORK

1

TIME/DISTANCE	REPS	RECOVERY

2

TIME/DISTANCE	REPS	RECOVERY

MOOD	LOW	1	2	3	4	5	6	7	8	9	10	HIGH
ENERGY	LOW	1	2	3	4	5	6	7	8	9	10	HIGH
NUTRITION		1	2	3	4	5	6	7	8	9	10	
WATER 8oz		1	2	3	4	5	6	7	8	9	10	

SLEEP DIARY

WEEK 3	DAY 4	DATE

RUN 1

TIME/DISTANCE	WEATHER

COMMENTS

BAD RUN	1	2	3	4	5	6	7	8	9	10	GOOD RUN

NUTRITION

BEFORE	DURING	AFTER

RUN 2

TIME/DISTANCE	WEATHER

COMMENTS

BAD RUN	1	2	3	4	5	6	7	8	9	10	GOOD RUN

NUTRITION

BEFORE	DURING	AFTER

SPEEDWORK

1

TIME/DISTANCE	REPS	RECOVERY

2

TIME/DISTANCE	REPS	RECOVERY

MOOD	LOW	1	2	3	4	5	6	7	8	9	10	HIGH
ENERGY	LOW	1	2	3	4	5	6	7	8	9	10	HIGH
NUTRITION		1	2	3	4	5	6	7	8	9	10	
WATER 8oz		1	2	3	4	5	6	7	8	9	10	

SLEEP DIARY

RUN JOURNAL

WEEK 3 | DAY 5 | DATE

RUN 1

TIME/DISTANCE	WEATHER

COMMENTS

BAD RUN 1 2 3 4 5 6 7 8 9 10 GOOD RUN

NUTRITION

BEFORE	DURING	AFTER

RUN 2

TIME/DISTANCE	WEATHER

COMMENTS

BAD RUN 1 2 3 4 5 6 7 8 9 10 GOOD RUN

NUTRITION

BEFORE	DURING	AFTER

SPEEDWORK

1

TIME/DISTANCE	REPS	RECOVERY

2

TIME/DISTANCE	REPS	RECOVERY

MOOD	LOW	1	2	3	4	5	6	7	8	9	10	HIGH
ENERGY	LOW	1	2	3	4	5	6	7	8	9	10	HIGH
NUTRITION		1	2	3	4	5	6	7	8	9	10	
WATER 8oz		1	2	3	4	5	6	7	8	9	10	

SLEEP DIARY

RUN 1

TIME/DISTANCE	WEATHER

COMMENTS

BAD RUN 1 2 3 4 5 6 7 8 9 10 GOOD RUN

NUTRITION

BEFORE	DURING	AFTER

RUN 2

TIME/DISTANCE	WEATHER

COMMENTS

BAD RUN 1 2 3 4 5 6 7 8 9 10 GOOD RUN

NUTRITION

BEFORE	DURING	AFTER

SPEEDWORK

1

TIME/DISTANCE	REPS	RECOVERY

2

TIME/DISTANCE	REPS	RECOVERY

MOOD	LOW	1	2	3	4	5	6	7	8	9	10	HIGH
ENERGY	LOW	1	2	3	4	5	6	7	8	9	10	HIGH
NUTRITION		1	2	3	4	5	6	7	8	9	10	
WATER 8oz		1	2	3	4	5	6	7	8	9	10	

SLEEP DIARY

RUN JOURNAL

WEEK 3 | DAY 7 | DATE

RUN 1

TIME/DISTANCE	WEATHER

COMMENTS

BAD RUN 1 2 3 4 5 6 7 8 9 10 GOOD RUN

NUTRITION

BEFORE	DURING	AFTER

RUN 2

TIME/DISTANCE	WEATHER

COMMENTS

BAD RUN 1 2 3 4 5 6 7 8 9 10 GOOD RUN

NUTRITION

BEFORE	DURING	AFTER

SPEEDWORK

1

TIME/DISTANCE	REPS	RECOVERY

2

TIME/DISTANCE	REPS	RECOVERY

MOOD	LOW	1	2	3	4	5	6	7	8	9	10	HIGH
ENERGY	LOW	1	2	3	4	5	6	7	8	9	10	HIGH
NUTRITION		1	2	3	4	5	6	7	8	9	10	
WATER 8oz		1	2	3	4	5	6	7	8	9	10	

SLEEP DIARY

WEEK 3 SUMMARY

DATE

GOALS MET

GOALS EXCEEDED

NEXT WEEK

RUNNING NOTES

SPEEDWORK NOTES

REFUELING NOTES

	Calories consumed	
MINUS	Calories Used	
EQUALS	Net Calories	
	BMR	
	net calories deficit	

VITAMINS	DOSAGE	QTY

MOOD

1 2 3 4 5 6 7 8 9 10

ENERGY LEVEL

1 2 3 4 5 6 7 8 9 10

Journal

RUN JOURNAL

WEEK 4 | DAY 1 | DATE

RUN 1

TIME/DISTANCE	WEATHER

COMMENTS

BAD RUN 1 2 3 4 5 6 7 8 9 10 GOOD RUN

NUTRITION

BEFORE	DURING	AFTER

RUN 2

TIME/DISTANCE	WEATHER

COMMENTS

BAD RUN 1 2 3 4 5 6 7 8 9 10 GOOD RUN

NUTRITION

BEFORE	DURING	AFTER

SPEEDWORK

1

TIME/DISTANCE	REPS	RECOVERY

2

TIME/DISTANCE	REPS	RECOVERY

MOOD	LOW	1	2	3	4	5	6	7	8	9	10	HIGH
ENERGY	LOW	1	2	3	4	5	6	7	8	9	10	HIGH
NUTRITION		1	2	3	4	5	6	7	8	9	10	
WATER 8oz		1	2	3	4	5	6	7	8	9	10	

SLEEP DIARY

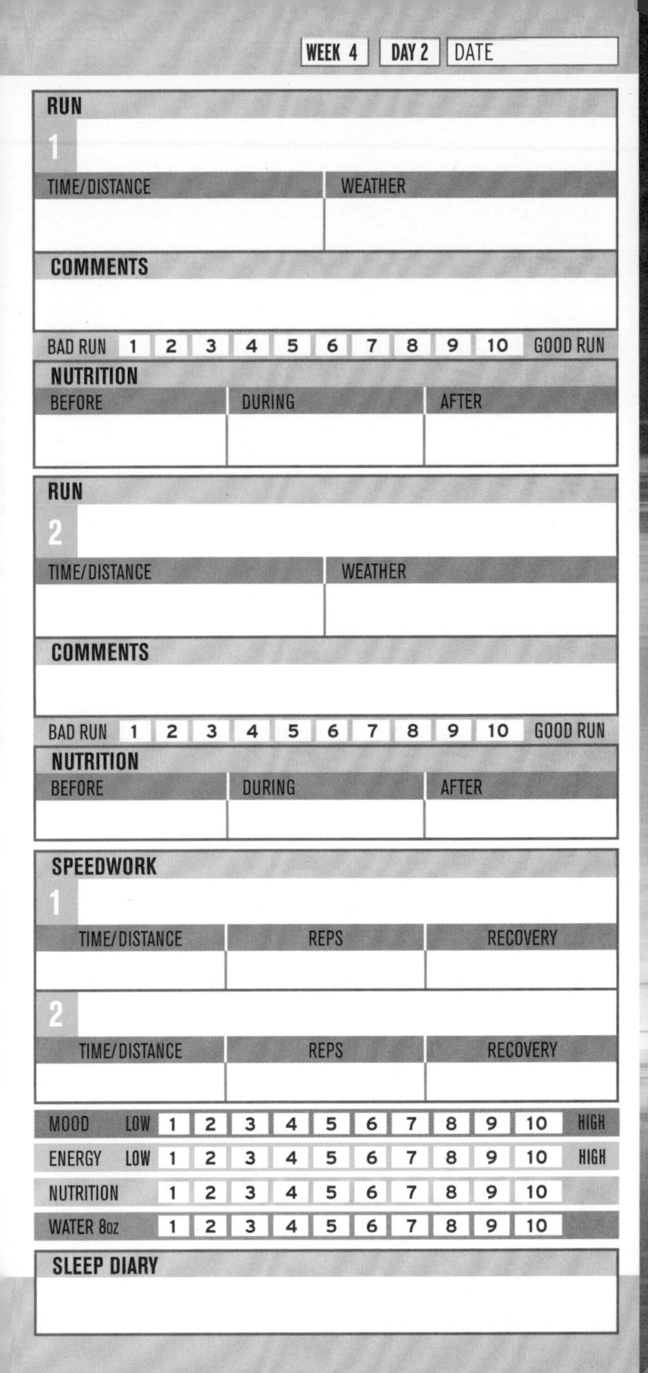

WEEK 4 | DAY 2 | DATE

RUN 1

TIME/DISTANCE	WEATHER

COMMENTS

BAD RUN	1	2	3	4	5	6	7	8	9	10	GOOD RUN

NUTRITION

BEFORE	DURING	AFTER

RUN 2

TIME/DISTANCE	WEATHER

COMMENTS

BAD RUN	1	2	3	4	5	6	7	8	9	10	GOOD RUN

NUTRITION

BEFORE	DURING	AFTER

SPEEDWORK

1

TIME/DISTANCE	REPS	RECOVERY

2

TIME/DISTANCE	REPS	RECOVERY

MOOD	LOW	1	2	3	4	5	6	7	8	9	10	HIGH
ENERGY	LOW	1	2	3	4	5	6	7	8	9	10	HIGH
NUTRITION		1	2	3	4	5	6	7	8	9	10	
WATER 8oz		1	2	3	4	5	6	7	8	9	10	

SLEEP DIARY

RUN JOURNAL

WEEK 4 | DAY 3 | DATE

RUN

1

TIME/DISTANCE	WEATHER

COMMENTS

BAD RUN 1 2 3 4 5 6 7 8 9 10 GOOD RUN

NUTRITION

BEFORE	DURING	AFTER

RUN

2

TIME/DISTANCE	WEATHER

COMMENTS

BAD RUN 1 2 3 4 5 6 7 8 9 10 GOOD RUN

NUTRITION

BEFORE	DURING	AFTER

SPEEDWORK

1

TIME/DISTANCE	REPS	RECOVERY

2

TIME/DISTANCE	REPS	RECOVERY

MOOD	LOW	1	2	3	4	5	6	7	8	9	10	HIGH
ENERGY	LOW	1	2	3	4	5	6	7	8	9	10	HIGH
NUTRITION		1	2	3	4	5	6	7	8	9	10	
WATER 8oz		1	2	3	4	5	6	7	8	9	10	

SLEEP DIARY

RUN 1

TIME/DISTANCE	WEATHER

COMMENTS

BAD RUN 1 2 3 4 5 6 7 8 9 10 GOOD RUN

NUTRITION

BEFORE	DURING	AFTER

RUN 2

TIME/DISTANCE	WEATHER

COMMENTS

BAD RUN 1 2 3 4 5 6 7 8 9 10 GOOD RUN

NUTRITION

BEFORE	DURING	AFTER

SPEEDWORK

1

TIME/DISTANCE	REPS	RECOVERY

2

TIME/DISTANCE	REPS	RECOVERY

MOOD	LOW	1	2	3	4	5	6	7	8	9	10	HIGH
ENERGY	LOW	1	2	3	4	5	6	7	8	9	10	HIGH
NUTRITION		1	2	3	4	5	6	7	8	9	10	
WATER 8oz		1	2	3	4	5	6	7	8	9	10	

SLEEP DIARY

RUN JOURNAL

WEEK 4 | DAY 5 | DATE

RUN 1

TIME/DISTANCE	WEATHER

COMMENTS

BAD RUN 1 2 3 4 5 6 7 8 9 10 GOOD RUN

NUTRITION

BEFORE	DURING	AFTER

RUN 2

TIME/DISTANCE	WEATHER

COMMENTS

BAD RUN 1 2 3 4 5 6 7 8 9 10 GOOD RUN

NUTRITION

BEFORE	DURING	AFTER

SPEEDWORK

1

TIME/DISTANCE	REPS	RECOVERY

2

TIME/DISTANCE	REPS	RECOVERY

MOOD	LOW	1	2	3	4	5	6	7	8	9	10	HIGH
ENERGY	LOW	1	2	3	4	5	6	7	8	9	10	HIGH
NUTRITION		1	2	3	4	5	6	7	8	9	10	
WATER 8oz		1	2	3	4	5	6	7	8	9	10	

SLEEP DIARY

WEEK 4 | DAY 6 | DATE

RUN

1

TIME/DISTANCE	WEATHER

COMMENTS

BAD RUN 1 2 3 4 5 6 7 8 9 10 GOOD RUN

NUTRITION

BEFORE	DURING	AFTER

RUN

2

TIME/DISTANCE	WEATHER

COMMENTS

BAD RUN 1 2 3 4 5 6 7 8 9 10 GOOD RUN

NUTRITION

BEFORE	DURING	AFTER

SPEEDWORK

1

TIME/DISTANCE	REPS	RECOVERY

2

TIME/DISTANCE	REPS	RECOVERY

MOOD	LOW	1	2	3	4	5	6	7	8	9	10	HIGH
ENERGY	LOW	1	2	3	4	5	6	7	8	9	10	HIGH
NUTRITION		1	2	3	4	5	6	7	8	9	10	
WATER 8oz		1	2	3	4	5	6	7	8	9	10	

SLEEP DIARY

RUN JOURNAL

WEEK 4 | DAY 7 | DATE

RUN

1

TIME/DISTANCE	WEATHER

COMMENTS

BAD RUN 1 2 3 4 5 6 7 8 9 10 GOOD RUN

NUTRITION

BEFORE	DURING	AFTER

RUN

2

TIME/DISTANCE	WEATHER

COMMENTS

BAD RUN 1 2 3 4 5 6 7 8 9 10 GOOD RUN

NUTRITION

BEFORE	DURING	AFTER

SPEEDWORK

1

TIME/DISTANCE	REPS	RECOVERY

2

TIME/DISTANCE	REPS	RECOVERY

MOOD	LOW	1	2	3	4	5	6	7	8	9	10	HIGH
ENERGY	LOW	1	2	3	4	5	6	7	8	9	10	HIGH
NUTRITION		1	2	3	4	5	6	7	8	9	10	
WATER 8oz		1	2	3	4	5	6	7	8	9	10	

SLEEP DIARY

WEEK 4 SUMMARY

DATE

GOALS MET

GOALS EXCEEDED

NEXT WEEK

RUNNING NOTES

SPEEDWORK NOTES

REFUELING NOTES

Calories consumed	
MINUS Calories Used	
EQUALS Net Calories	
BMR	
net calories deficit	

MOOD

1 2 3 4 5 6 7 8 9 10

ENERGY LEVEL

1 2 3 4 5 6 7 8 9 10

VITAMINS	DOSAGE	QTY

Journal

RUN JOURNAL

MONTH 1 | DATE

MONTH 1 SUMMARY

GOALS MET ☐ GOALS EXCEEDED ☐ MAYBE NEXT WEEK ☐

RUNNING NOTES

SPEEDWORK NOTES

MOOD & ENERGY

TOTAL RUNNING SESSIONS ☐

TOTAL SPEEDWORK SESSIONS ☐

GOALS FOR NEXT MONTH

RUN TRAINING GOALS

SPEED TRAINING GOALS

STAY HYDRATED

If you're looking for a basic guideline for fluid consumption during your runs: You should drink 4 to 6 ounces of water every 20 minutes during your runs. Runners who run faster than 8-minute miles should drink 6 to 8 ounces every 20 minutes. During workouts longer than 90 minutes some of your fluid intake should include a sports drink to replace lost sodium and other minerals (electrolytes). The carbohydrates and electrolytes in the sports drink also help you absorb the fluids faster.

RUN JOURNAL

WEEK 5 | DAY 1 | DATE

RUN 1

TIME/DISTANCE	WEATHER

COMMENTS

BAD RUN 1 2 3 4 5 6 7 8 9 10 GOOD RUN

NUTRITION

BEFORE	DURING	AFTER

RUN 2

TIME/DISTANCE	WEATHER

COMMENTS

BAD RUN 1 2 3 4 5 6 7 8 9 10 GOOD RUN

NUTRITION

BEFORE	DURING	AFTER

SPEEDWORK

1

TIME/DISTANCE	REPS	RECOVERY

2

TIME/DISTANCE	REPS	RECOVERY

MOOD	LOW	1	2	3	4	5	6	7	8	9	10	HIGH
ENERGY	LOW	1	2	3	4	5	6	7	8	9	10	HIGH
NUTRITION		1	2	3	4	5	6	7	8	9	10	
WATER 8oz		1	2	3	4	5	6	7	8	9	10	

SLEEP DIARY

WEEK 5 | DAY 2 | DATE

RUN 1

TIME/DISTANCE	WEATHER

COMMENTS

BAD RUN 1 2 3 4 5 6 7 8 9 10 GOOD RUN

NUTRITION

BEFORE	DURING	AFTER

RUN 2

TIME/DISTANCE	WEATHER

COMMENTS

BAD RUN 1 2 3 4 5 6 7 8 9 10 GOOD RUN

NUTRITION

BEFORE	DURING	AFTER

SPEEDWORK

1

TIME/DISTANCE	REPS	RECOVERY

2

TIME/DISTANCE	REPS	RECOVERY

MOOD	LOW	1	2	3	4	5	6	7	8	9	10	HIGH
ENERGY	LOW	1	2	3	4	5	6	7	8	9	10	HIGH
NUTRITION		1	2	3	4	5	6	7	8	9	10	
WATER 8oz		1	2	3	4	5	6	7	8	9	10	

SLEEP DIARY

RUN JOURNAL

WEEK 5 | DAY 3 | DATE

RUN 1

TIME/DISTANCE	WEATHER

COMMENTS

BAD RUN 1 2 3 4 5 6 7 8 9 10 GOOD RUN

NUTRITION

BEFORE	DURING	AFTER

RUN 2

TIME/DISTANCE	WEATHER

COMMENTS

BAD RUN 1 2 3 4 5 6 7 8 9 10 GOOD RUN

NUTRITION

BEFORE	DURING	AFTER

SPEEDWORK

1

TIME/DISTANCE	REPS	RECOVERY

2

TIME/DISTANCE	REPS	RECOVERY

MOOD	LOW	1	2	3	4	5	6	7	8	9	10	HIGH
ENERGY	LOW	1	2	3	4	5	6	7	8	9	10	HIGH
NUTRITION		1	2	3	4	5	6	7	8	9	10	
WATER 8oz		1	2	3	4	5	6	7	8	9	10	

SLEEP DIARY

RUN 1

TIME/DISTANCE	WEATHER

COMMENTS

BAD RUN 1 2 3 4 5 6 7 8 9 10 GOOD RUN

NUTRITION

BEFORE	DURING	AFTER

RUN 2

TIME/DISTANCE	WEATHER

COMMENTS

BAD RUN 1 2 3 4 5 6 7 8 9 10 GOOD RUN

NUTRITION

BEFORE	DURING	AFTER

SPEEDWORK

1

TIME/DISTANCE	REPS	RECOVERY

2

TIME/DISTANCE	REPS	RECOVERY

MOOD	LOW	1	2	3	4	5	6	7	8	9	10	HIGH
ENERGY	LOW	1	2	3	4	5	6	7	8	9	10	HIGH
NUTRITION		1	2	3	4	5	6	7	8	9	10	
WATER 8oz		1	2	3	4	5	6	7	8	9	10	

SLEEP DIARY

RUN JOURNAL

WEEK 5 | DAY 5 | DATE

RUN 1

TIME/DISTANCE	WEATHER

COMMENTS

BAD RUN	1	2	3	4	5	6	7	8	9	10	GOOD RUN

NUTRITION

BEFORE	DURING	AFTER

RUN 2

TIME/DISTANCE	WEATHER

COMMENTS

BAD RUN	1	2	3	4	5	6	7	8	9	10	GOOD RUN

NUTRITION

BEFORE	DURING	AFTER

SPEEDWORK

1

TIME/DISTANCE	REPS	RECOVERY

2

TIME/DISTANCE	REPS	RECOVERY

MOOD	LOW	1	2	3	4	5	6	7	8	9	10	HIGH
ENERGY	LOW	1	2	3	4	5	6	7	8	9	10	HIGH
NUTRITION		1	2	3	4	5	6	7	8	9	10	
WATER 8oz		1	2	3	4	5	6	7	8	9	10	

SLEEP DIARY

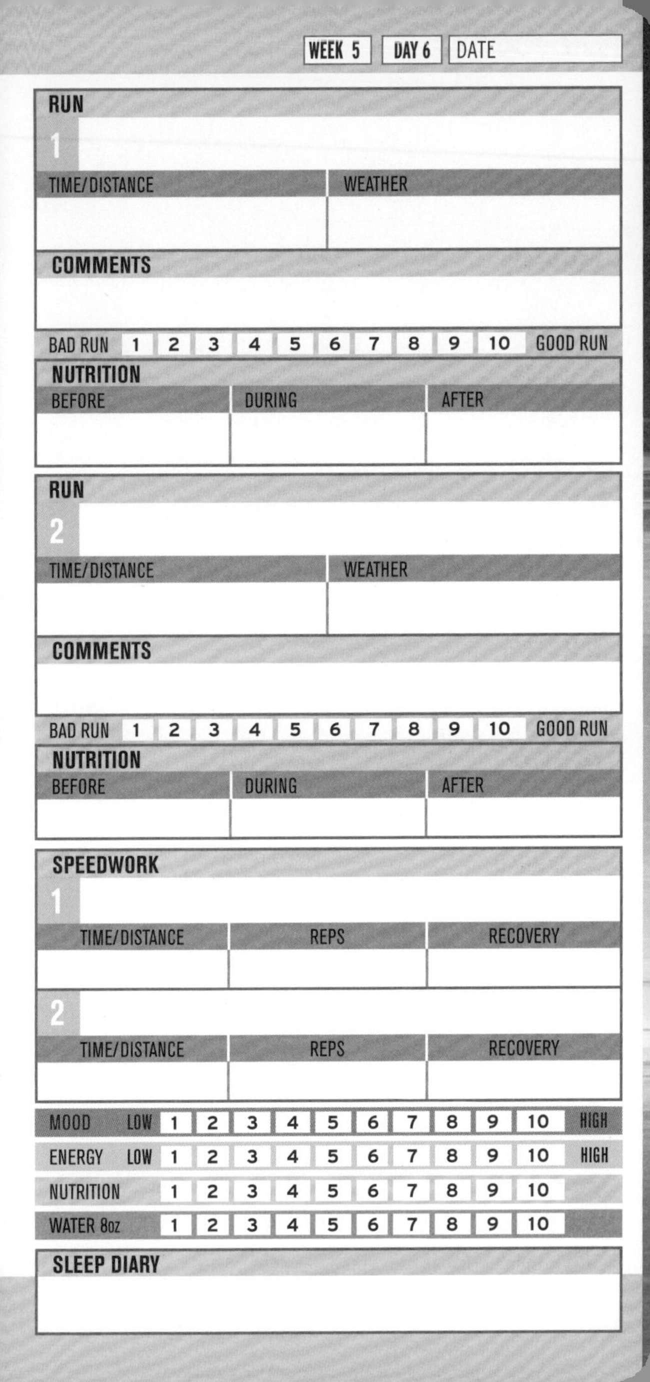

WEEK 5 | DAY 6 | DATE

RUN 1

TIME/DISTANCE	WEATHER

COMMENTS

BAD RUN 1 2 3 4 5 6 7 8 9 10 GOOD RUN

NUTRITION

BEFORE	DURING	AFTER

RUN 2

TIME/DISTANCE	WEATHER

COMMENTS

BAD RUN 1 2 3 4 5 6 7 8 9 10 GOOD RUN

NUTRITION

BEFORE	DURING	AFTER

SPEEDWORK

1

TIME/DISTANCE	REPS	RECOVERY

2

TIME/DISTANCE	REPS	RECOVERY

MOOD LOW 1 2 3 4 5 6 7 8 9 10 HIGH

ENERGY LOW 1 2 3 4 5 6 7 8 9 10 HIGH

NUTRITION 1 2 3 4 5 6 7 8 9 10

WATER 8oz 1 2 3 4 5 6 7 8 9 10

SLEEP DIARY

RUN JOURNAL

WEEK 5 | DAY 7 | DATE

RUN 1

TIME/DISTANCE	WEATHER

COMMENTS

BAD RUN 1 2 3 4 5 6 7 8 9 10 GOOD RUN

NUTRITION

BEFORE	DURING	AFTER

RUN 2

TIME/DISTANCE	WEATHER

COMMENTS

BAD RUN 1 2 3 4 5 6 7 8 9 10 GOOD RUN

NUTRITION

BEFORE	DURING	AFTER

SPEEDWORK

1

TIME/DISTANCE	REPS	RECOVERY

2

TIME/DISTANCE	REPS	RECOVERY

MOOD	LOW	1	2	3	4	5	6	7	8	9	10	HIGH
ENERGY	LOW	1	2	3	4	5	6	7	8	9	10	HIGH
NUTRITION		1	2	3	4	5	6	7	8	9	10	
WATER 8oz		1	2	3	4	5	6	7	8	9	10	

SLEEP DIARY

WEEK 5 SUMMARY

DATE

GOALS MET

GOALS EXCEEDED

NEXT WEEK

RUNNING NOTES

SPEEDWORK NOTES

REFUELING NOTES

	Calories consumed	
MINUS	Calories Used	
EQUALS	Net Calories	
	BMR	
	net calories deficit	

VITAMINS	DOSAGE	QTY

MOOD

1 2 3 4 5 6 7 8 9 10

ENERGY LEVEL

1 2 3 4 5 6 7 8 9 10

Journal

RUN JOURNAL

WEEK 6 | DAY 1 | DATE

RUN

1

TIME/DISTANCE	WEATHER

COMMENTS

BAD RUN 1 2 3 4 5 6 7 8 9 10 GOOD RUN

NUTRITION

BEFORE	DURING	AFTER

RUN

2

TIME/DISTANCE	WEATHER

COMMENTS

BAD RUN 1 2 3 4 5 6 7 8 9 10 GOOD RUN

NUTRITION

BEFORE	DURING	AFTER

SPEEDWORK

1

TIME/DISTANCE	REPS	RECOVERY

2

TIME/DISTANCE	REPS	RECOVERY

MOOD	LOW	1	2	3	4	5	6	7	8	9	10	HIGH
ENERGY	LOW	1	2	3	4	5	6	7	8	9	10	HIGH
NUTRITION		1	2	3	4	5	6	7	8	9	10	
WATER 8oz		1	2	3	4	5	6	7	8	9	10	

SLEEP DIARY

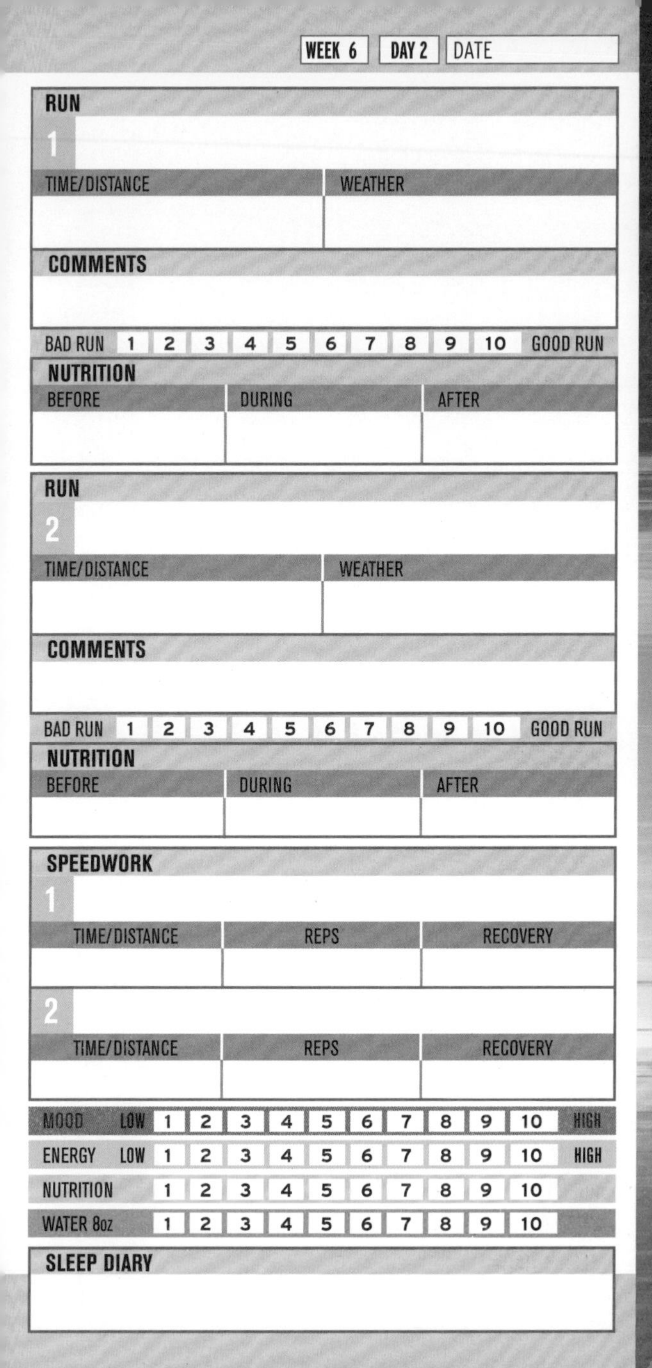

WEEK 6 | DAY 2 | DATE

RUN

1

TIME/DISTANCE	WEATHER

COMMENTS

BAD RUN 1 2 3 4 5 6 7 8 9 10 GOOD RUN

NUTRITION

BEFORE	DURING	AFTER

RUN

2

TIME/DISTANCE	WEATHER

COMMENTS

BAD RUN 1 2 3 4 5 6 7 8 9 10 GOOD RUN

NUTRITION

BEFORE	DURING	AFTER

SPEEDWORK

1

TIME/DISTANCE	REPS	RECOVERY

2

TIME/DISTANCE	REPS	RECOVERY

MOOD	LOW	1	2	3	4	5	6	7	8	9	10	HIGH
ENERGY	LOW	1	2	3	4	5	6	7	8	9	10	HIGH
NUTRITION		1	2	3	4	5	6	7	8	9	10	
WATER 8oz		1	2	3	4	5	6	7	8	9	10	

SLEEP DIARY

RUN JOURNAL

WEEK 6 | DAY 3 | DATE

RUN 1

TIME/DISTANCE	WEATHER

COMMENTS

BAD RUN 1 2 3 4 5 6 7 8 9 10 GOOD RUN

NUTRITION

BEFORE	DURING	AFTER

RUN 2

TIME/DISTANCE	WEATHER

COMMENTS

BAD RUN 1 2 3 4 5 6 7 8 9 10 GOOD RUN

NUTRITION

BEFORE	DURING	AFTER

SPEEDWORK

1

TIME/DISTANCE	REPS	RECOVERY

2

TIME/DISTANCE	REPS	RECOVERY

MOOD	LOW	1	2	3	4	5	6	7	8	9	10	HIGH
ENERGY	LOW	1	2	3	4	5	6	7	8	9	10	HIGH
NUTRITION		1	2	3	4	5	6	7	8	9	10	
WATER 8oz		1	2	3	4	5	6	7	8	9	10	

SLEEP DIARY

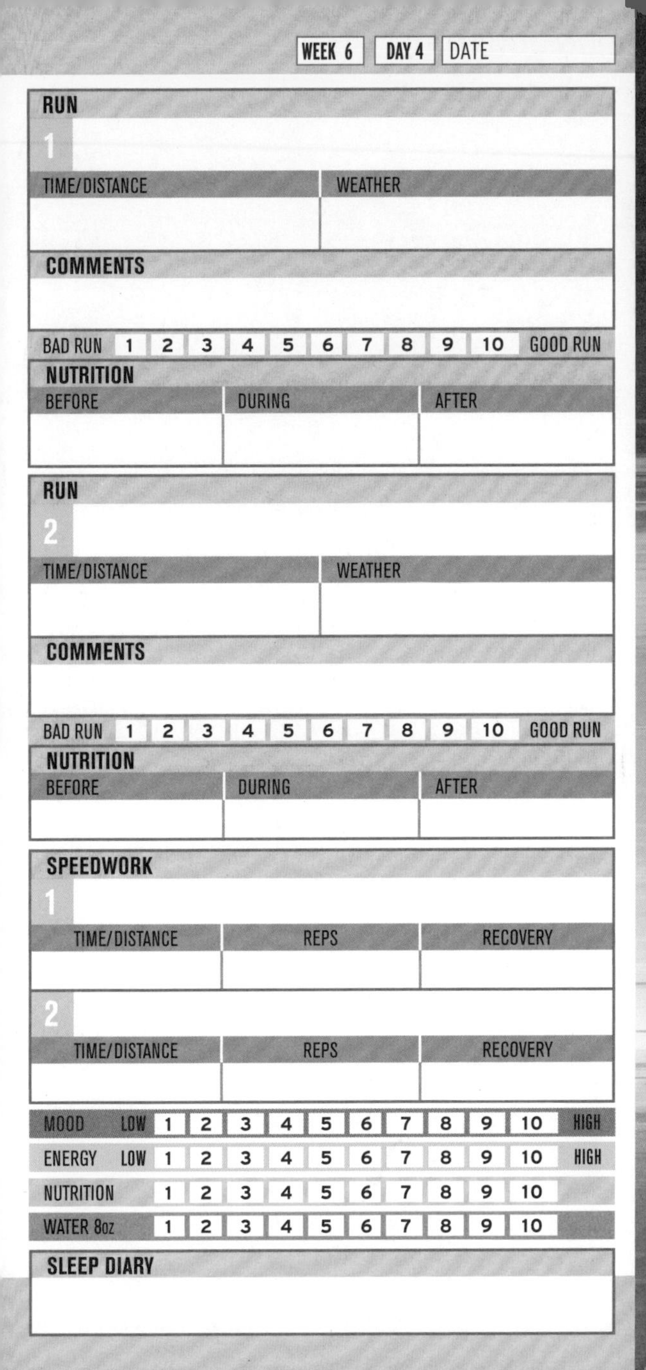

WEEK 6
DAY 4
DATE
RUN
1
TIME/DISTANCE
WEATHER
COMMENTS
BAD RUN 1 2 3 4 5 6 7 8 9 10 GOOD RUN
NUTRITION
BEFORE
DURING
AFTER
RUN
2
TIME/DISTANCE
WEATHER
COMMENTS
BAD RUN 1 2 3 4 5 6 7 8 9 10 GOOD RUN
NUTRITION
BEFORE
DURING
AFTER
SPEEDWORK
1
TIME/DISTANCE
REPS
RECOVERY
2
TIME/DISTANCE
REPS
RECOVERY
MOOD LOW 1 2 3 4 5 6 7 8 9 10 HIGH
ENERGY LOW 1 2 3 4 5 6 7 8 9 10 HIGH
NUTRITION 1 2 3 4 5 6 7 8 9 10
WATER 8oz 1 2 3 4 5 6 7 8 9 10
SLEEP DIARY

RUN JOURNAL

WEEK 6 | DAY 5 | DATE

RUN 1

TIME/DISTANCE	WEATHER

COMMENTS

BAD RUN 1 2 3 4 5 6 7 8 9 10 GOOD RUN

NUTRITION

BEFORE	DURING	AFTER

RUN 2

TIME/DISTANCE	WEATHER

COMMENTS

BAD RUN 1 2 3 4 5 6 7 8 9 10 GOOD RUN

NUTRITION

BEFORE	DURING	AFTER

SPEEDWORK

1

TIME/DISTANCE	REPS	RECOVERY

2

TIME/DISTANCE	REPS	RECOVERY

MOOD	LOW	1	2	3	4	5	6	7	8	9	10	HIGH
ENERGY	LOW	1	2	3	4	5	6	7	8	9	10	HIGH
NUTRITION		1	2	3	4	5	6	7	8	9	10	
WATER 8oz		1	2	3	4	5	6	7	8	9	10	

SLEEP DIARY

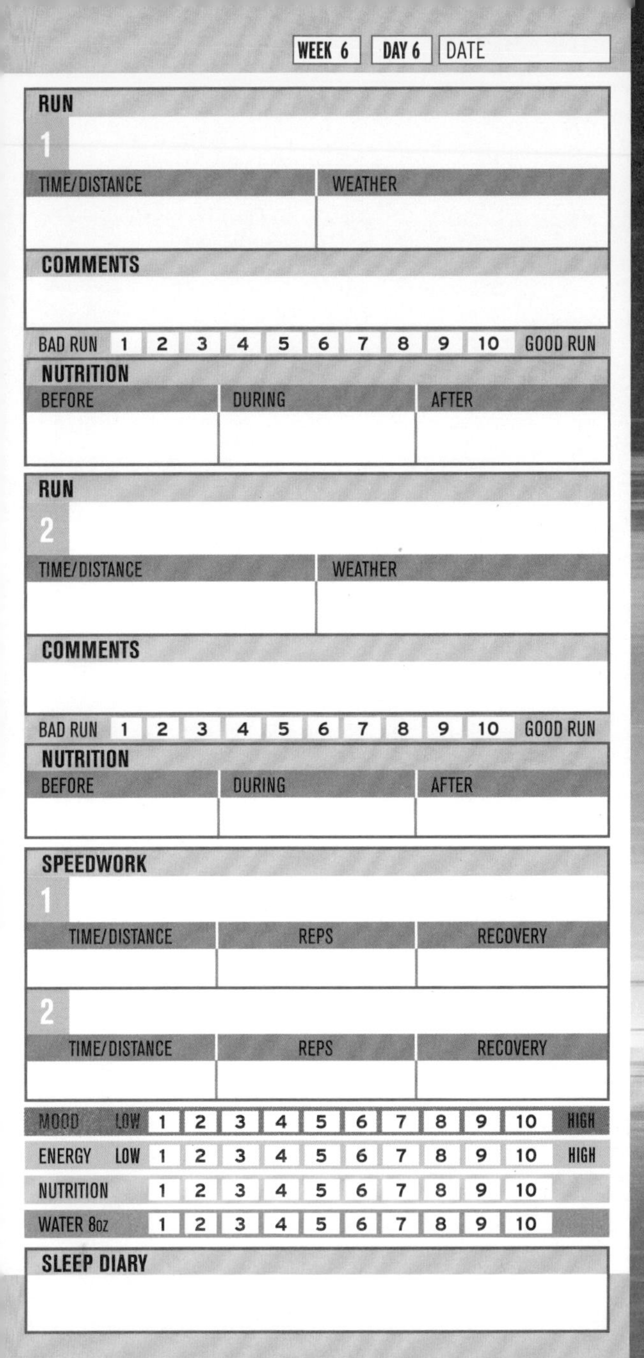

WEEK 6 | DAY 6 | DATE

RUN 1

TIME/DISTANCE	WEATHER

COMMENTS

BAD RUN 1 2 3 4 5 6 7 8 9 10 GOOD RUN

NUTRITION

BEFORE	DURING	AFTER

RUN 2

TIME/DISTANCE	WEATHER

COMMENTS

BAD RUN 1 2 3 4 5 6 7 8 9 10 GOOD RUN

NUTRITION

BEFORE	DURING	AFTER

SPEEDWORK

1

TIME/DISTANCE	REPS	RECOVERY

2

TIME/DISTANCE	REPS	RECOVERY

MOOD	LOW	1	2	3	4	5	6	7	8	9	10	HIGH
ENERGY	LOW	1	2	3	4	5	6	7	8	9	10	HIGH
NUTRITION		1	2	3	4	5	6	7	8	9	10	
WATER 8oz		1	2	3	4	5	6	7	8	9	10	

SLEEP DIARY

RUN JOURNAL

WEEK 6 | DAY 7 | DATE

RUN

1

TIME/DISTANCE	WEATHER

COMMENTS

BAD RUN 1 2 3 4 5 6 7 8 9 10 GOOD RUN

NUTRITION

BEFORE	DURING	AFTER

RUN

2

TIME/DISTANCE	WEATHER

COMMENTS

BAD RUN 1 2 3 4 5 6 7 8 9 10 GOOD RUN

NUTRITION

BEFORE	DURING	AFTER

SPEEDWORK

1

TIME/DISTANCE	REPS	RECOVERY

2

TIME/DISTANCE	REPS	RECOVERY

MOOD	LOW	1	2	3	4	5	6	7	8	9	10	HIGH
ENERGY	LOW	1	2	3	4	5	6	7	8	9	10	HIGH
NUTRITION		1	2	3	4	5	6	7	8	9	10	
WATER 8oz		1	2	3	4	5	6	7	8	9	10	

SLEEP DIARY

WEEK 6 SUMMARY

DATE

GOALS MET

GOALS EXCEEDED

NEXT WEEK

RUNNING NOTES

SPEEDWORK NOTES

REFUELING NOTES

	Calories consumed	
MINUS	Calories Used	
EQUALS	Net Calories	
	BMR	
	net calories deficit	

VITAMINS	DOSAGE	QTY

MOOD

1 2 3 4 5 6 7 8 9 10

ENERGY LEVEL

1 2 3 4 5 6 7 8 9 10

Journal

RUN JOURNAL

WEEK 7 | DAY 1 | DATE

RUN 1

TIME/DISTANCE	WEATHER

COMMENTS

BAD RUN 1 2 3 4 5 6 7 8 9 10 GOOD RUN

NUTRITION

BEFORE	DURING	AFTER

RUN 2

TIME/DISTANCE	WEATHER

COMMENTS

BAD RUN 1 2 3 4 5 6 7 8 9 10 GOOD RUN

NUTRITION

BEFORE	DURING	AFTER

SPEEDWORK

1

TIME/DISTANCE	REPS	RECOVERY

2

TIME/DISTANCE	REPS	RECOVERY

MOOD	LOW	1	2	3	4	5	6	7	8	9	10	HIGH
ENERGY	LOW	1	2	3	4	5	6	7	8	9	10	HIGH
NUTRITION		1	2	3	4	5	6	7	8	9	10	
WATER 8oz		1	2	3	4	5	6	7	8	9	10	

SLEEP DIARY

WEEK 7 | DAY 2 | DATE

RUN

1

TIME/DISTANCE	WEATHER

COMMENTS

BAD RUN 1 2 3 4 5 6 7 8 9 10 GOOD RUN

NUTRITION

BEFORE	DURING	AFTER

RUN

2

TIME/DISTANCE	WEATHER

COMMENTS

BAD RUN 1 2 3 4 5 6 7 8 9 10 GOOD RUN

NUTRITION

BEFORE	DURING	AFTER

SPEEDWORK

1

TIME/DISTANCE	REPS	RECOVERY

2

TIME/DISTANCE	REPS	RECOVERY

MOOD	LOW	1	2	3	4	5	6	7	8	9	10	HIGH
ENERGY	LOW	1	2	3	4	5	6	7	8	9	10	HIGH
NUTRITION		1	2	3	4	5	6	7	8	9	10	
WATER 8oz		1	2	3	4	5	6	7	8	9	10	

SLEEP DIARY

RUN JOURNAL

WEEK 7 | DAY 3 | DATE

RUN 1

TIME/DISTANCE	WEATHER

COMMENTS

BAD RUN 1 2 3 4 5 6 7 8 9 10 GOOD RUN

NUTRITION

BEFORE	DURING	AFTER

RUN 2

TIME/DISTANCE	WEATHER

COMMENTS

BAD RUN 1 2 3 4 5 6 7 8 9 10 GOOD RUN

NUTRITION

BEFORE	DURING	AFTER

SPEEDWORK

1

TIME/DISTANCE	REPS	RECOVERY

2

TIME/DISTANCE	REPS	RECOVERY

MOOD	LOW	1	2	3	4	5	6	7	8	9	10	HIGH
ENERGY	LOW	1	2	3	4	5	6	7	8	9	10	HIGH
NUTRITION		1	2	3	4	5	6	7	8	9	10	
WATER 8oz		1	2	3	4	5	6	7	8	9	10	

SLEEP DIARY

WEEK 7 | DAY 4 | DATE

RUN 1

TIME/DISTANCE	WEATHER

COMMENTS

BAD RUN 1 2 3 4 5 6 7 8 9 10 GOOD RUN

NUTRITION

BEFORE	DURING	AFTER

RUN 2

TIME/DISTANCE	WEATHER

COMMENTS

BAD RUN 1 2 3 4 5 6 7 8 9 10 GOOD RUN

NUTRITION

BEFORE	DURING	AFTER

SPEEDWORK

1

TIME/DISTANCE	REPS	RECOVERY

2

TIME/DISTANCE	REPS	RECOVERY

MOOD	LOW	1	2	3	4	5	6	7	8	9	10	HIGH
ENERGY	LOW	1	2	3	4	5	6	7	8	9	10	HIGH
NUTRITION		1	2	3	4	5	6	7	8	9	10	
WATER 8oz		1	2	3	4	5	6	7	8	9	10	

SLEEP DIARY

RUN JOURNAL

WEEK 7 | DAY 5 | DATE

RUN

1

TIME/DISTANCE	WEATHER

COMMENTS

BAD RUN 1 2 3 4 5 6 7 8 9 10 GOOD RUN

NUTRITION

BEFORE	DURING	AFTER

RUN

2

TIME/DISTANCE	WEATHER

COMMENTS

BAD RUN 1 2 3 4 5 6 7 8 9 10 GOOD RUN

NUTRITION

BEFORE	DURING	AFTER

SPEEDWORK

1

TIME/DISTANCE	REPS	RECOVERY

2

TIME/DISTANCE	REPS	RECOVERY

MOOD	LOW	1	2	3	4	5	6	7	8	9	10	HIGH
ENERGY	LOW	1	2	3	4	5	6	7	8	9	10	HIGH
NUTRITION		1	2	3	4	5	6	7	8	9	10	
WATER 8oz		1	2	3	4	5	6	7	8	9	10	

SLEEP DIARY

WEEK 7 | DAY 6 | DATE

RUN 1

TIME/DISTANCE	WEATHER

COMMENTS

BAD RUN 1 2 3 4 5 6 7 8 9 10 GOOD RUN

NUTRITION

BEFORE	DURING	AFTER

RUN 2

TIME/DISTANCE	WEATHER

COMMENTS

BAD RUN 1 2 3 4 5 6 7 8 9 10 GOOD RUN

NUTRITION

BEFORE	DURING	AFTER

SPEEDWORK

1

TIME/DISTANCE	REPS	RECOVERY

2

TIME/DISTANCE	REPS	RECOVERY

MOOD	LOW	1	2	3	4	5	6	7	8	9	10	HIGH
ENERGY	LOW	1	2	3	4	5	6	7	8	9	10	HIGH
NUTRITION		1	2	3	4	5	6	7	8	9	10	
WATER 8oz		1	2	3	4	5	6	7	8	9	10	

SLEEP DIARY

RUN JOURNAL

WEEK 7 | DAY 7 | DATE

RUN 1

TIME/DISTANCE	WEATHER

COMMENTS

BAD RUN 1 2 3 4 5 6 7 8 9 10 GOOD RUN

NUTRITION

BEFORE	DURING	AFTER

RUN 2

TIME/DISTANCE	WEATHER

COMMENTS

BAD RUN 1 2 3 4 5 6 7 8 9 10 GOOD RUN

NUTRITION

BEFORE	DURING	AFTER

SPEEDWORK

1

TIME/DISTANCE	REPS	RECOVERY

2

TIME/DISTANCE	REPS	RECOVERY

MOOD	LOW	1	2	3	4	5	6	7	8	9	10	HIGH
ENERGY	LOW	1	2	3	4	5	6	7	8	9	10	HIGH
NUTRITION		1	2	3	4	5	6	7	8	9	10	
WATER 8oz		1	2	3	4	5	6	7	8	9	10	

SLEEP DIARY

WEEK 7 SUMMARY

DATE

GOALS MET

GOALS EXCEEDED

NEXT WEEK

RUNNING NOTES

SPEEDWORK NOTES

REFUELING NOTES

	Calories consumed	
MINUS	Calories Used	
EQUALS	Net Calories	
	BMR	
	net calories deficit	

VITAMINS	DOSAGE	QTY

MOOD

1 2 3 4 5 6 7 8 9 10

ENERGY LEVEL

1 2 3 4 5 6 7 8 9 10

Journal

RUN JOURNAL

WEEK 8 | DAY 1 | DATE

RUN 1

TIME/DISTANCE	WEATHER

COMMENTS

BAD RUN 1 2 3 4 5 6 7 8 9 10 GOOD RUN

NUTRITION

BEFORE	DURING	AFTER

RUN 2

TIME/DISTANCE	WEATHER

COMMENTS

BAD RUN 1 2 3 4 5 6 7 8 9 10 GOOD RUN

NUTRITION

BEFORE	DURING	AFTER

SPEEDWORK

1

TIME/DISTANCE	REPS	RECOVERY

2

TIME/DISTANCE	REPS	RECOVERY

MOOD	LOW	1	2	3	4	5	6	7	8	9	10	HIGH
ENERGY	LOW	1	2	3	4	5	6	7	8	9	10	HIGH
NUTRITION		1	2	3	4	5	6	7	8	9	10	
WATER 8oz		1	2	3	4	5	6	7	8	9	10	

SLEEP DIARY

WEEK 8 | DAY 2 | DATE

RUN 1

TIME/DISTANCE	WEATHER

COMMENTS

BAD RUN 1 2 3 4 5 6 7 8 9 10 GOOD RUN

NUTRITION

BEFORE	DURING	AFTER

RUN 2

TIME/DISTANCE	WEATHER

COMMENTS

BAD RUN 1 2 3 4 5 6 7 8 9 10 GOOD RUN

NUTRITION

BEFORE	DURING	AFTER

SPEEDWORK

1

TIME/DISTANCE	REPS	RECOVERY

2

TIME/DISTANCE	REPS	RECOVERY

MOOD	LOW	1	2	3	4	5	6	7	8	9	10	HIGH
ENERGY	LOW	1	2	3	4	5	6	7	8	9	10	HIGH
NUTRITION		1	2	3	4	5	6	7	8	9	10	
WATER 8oz		1	2	3	4	5	6	7	8	9	10	

SLEEP DIARY

RUN JOURNAL

WEEK 8 | DAY 3 | DATE

RUN 1

TIME/DISTANCE | WEATHER

COMMENTS

BAD RUN 1 2 3 4 5 6 7 8 9 10 GOOD RUN

NUTRITION

BEFORE | DURING | AFTER

RUN 2

TIME/DISTANCE | WEATHER

COMMENTS

BAD RUN 1 2 3 4 5 6 7 8 9 10 GOOD RUN

NUTRITION

BEFORE | DURING | AFTER

SPEEDWORK

1

TIME/DISTANCE	REPS	RECOVERY

2

TIME/DISTANCE	REPS	RECOVERY

MOOD	LOW	1	2	3	4	5	6	7	8	9	10	HIGH
ENERGY	LOW	1	2	3	4	5	6	7	8	9	10	HIGH
NUTRITION		1	2	3	4	5	6	7	8	9	10	
WATER 8oz		1	2	3	4	5	6	7	8	9	10	

SLEEP DIARY

WEEK 8 | DAY 4 | DATE

RUN

1

TIME/DISTANCE	WEATHER

COMMENTS

BAD RUN	1	2	3	4	5	6	7	8	9	10	GOOD RUN

NUTRITION

BEFORE	DURING	AFTER

RUN

2

TIME/DISTANCE	WEATHER

COMMENTS

BAD RUN	1	2	3	4	5	6	7	8	9	10	GOOD RUN

NUTRITION

BEFORE	DURING	AFTER

SPEEDWORK

1

TIME/DISTANCE	REPS	RECOVERY

2

TIME/DISTANCE	REPS	RECOVERY

MOOD	LOW	1	2	3	4	5	6	7	8	9	10	HIGH
ENERGY	LOW	1	2	3	4	5	6	7	8	9	10	HIGH
NUTRITION		1	2	3	4	5	6	7	8	9	10	
WATER 8oz		1	2	3	4	5	6	7	8	9	10	

SLEEP DIARY

RUN JOURNAL

WEEK 8 | DAY 5 | DATE

RUN 1

TIME/DISTANCE	WEATHER

COMMENTS

BAD RUN 1 2 3 4 5 6 7 8 9 10 GOOD RUN

NUTRITION

BEFORE	DURING	AFTER

RUN 2

TIME/DISTANCE	WEATHER

COMMENTS

BAD RUN 1 2 3 4 5 6 7 8 9 10 GOOD RUN

NUTRITION

BEFORE	DURING	AFTER

SPEEDWORK

1

TIME/DISTANCE	REPS	RECOVERY

2

TIME/DISTANCE	REPS	RECOVERY

MOOD	LOW	1	2	3	4	5	6	7	8	9	10	HIGH
ENERGY	LOW	1	2	3	4	5	6	7	8	9	10	HIGH
NUTRITION		1	2	3	4	5	6	7	8	9	10	
WATER 8oz		1	2	3	4	5	6	7	8	9	10	

SLEEP DIARY

WEEK 8	DAY 6	DATE

RUN 1

TIME/DISTANCE	WEATHER

COMMENTS

BAD RUN 1 2 3 4 5 6 7 8 9 10 GOOD RUN

NUTRITION

BEFORE	DURING	AFTER

RUN 2

TIME/DISTANCE	WEATHER

COMMENTS

BAD RUN 1 2 3 4 5 6 7 8 9 10 GOOD RUN

NUTRITION

BEFORE	DURING	AFTER

SPEEDWORK

1

TIME/DISTANCE	REPS	RECOVERY

2

TIME/DISTANCE	REPS	RECOVERY

MOOD	LOW	1	2	3	4	5	6	7	8	9	10	HIGH
ENERGY	LOW	1	2	3	4	5	6	7	8	9	10	HIGH
NUTRITION		1	2	3	4	5	6	7	8	9	10	
WATER 8oz		1	2	3	4	5	6	7	8	9	10	

SLEEP DIARY

RUN JOURNAL

WEEK 8 | DAY 7 | DATE

RUN

1

TIME/DISTANCE	WEATHER

COMMENTS

BAD RUN 1 2 3 4 5 6 7 8 9 10 GOOD RUN

NUTRITION

BEFORE	DURING	AFTER

RUN

2

TIME/DISTANCE	WEATHER

COMMENTS

BAD RUN 1 2 3 4 5 6 7 8 9 10 GOOD RUN

NUTRITION

BEFORE	DURING	AFTER

SPEEDWORK

1

TIME/DISTANCE	REPS	RECOVERY

2

TIME/DISTANCE	REPS	RECOVERY

MOOD	LOW	1	2	3	4	5	6	7	8	9	10	HIGH
ENERGY	LOW	1	2	3	4	5	6	7	8	9	10	HIGH
NUTRITION		1	2	3	4	5	6	7	8	9	10	
WATER 8oz		1	2	3	4	5	6	7	8	9	10	

SLEEP DIARY

WEEK 8 SUMMARY

DATE

GOALS MET

GOALS EXCEEDED

NEXT WEEK

RUNNING NOTES

SPEEDWORK NOTES

REFUELING NOTES

Calories consumed	
MINUS Calories Used	
EQUALS Net Calories	
BMR	
net calories deficit	

MOOD
1 2 3 4 5 6 7 8 9 10

ENERGY LEVEL
1 2 3 4 5 6 7 8 9 10

VITAMINS	DOSAGE	QTY

Journal

RUN JOURNAL

MONTH 2 | DATE

MONTH 2 SUMMARY

GOALS MET ____ GOALS EXCEEDED ____ MAYBE NEXT WEEK ____

RUNNING NOTES

SPEEDWORK NOTES

MOOD & ENERGY

TOTAL RUNNING SESSIONS ____

TOTAL SPEEDWORK SESSIONS ____

GOALS FOR NEXT MONTH

RUN TRAINING GOALS	SPEED TRAINING GOALS

SPEEDWORK

Use the following speed workout as a basis of how to build your own workouts:

400-metre Intervals

(1) Stretch and warm up completely with an easy 1 mile run.

(2) Run 3 sets of 4 x 400 metres (¼ mile) intervals (for a total of 12 x 400 metres) at 10-12% faster than race pace.

(3) Walk/jog 200 metres (⅛ mile) between intervals, and rest 5:00 minutes between sets.

(4) Cool down with an easy 1 mile run.

RUN JOURNAL

WEEK 9 | DAY 1 | DATE

RUN 1

TIME/DISTANCE	WEATHER

COMMENTS

BAD RUN	1	2	3	4	5	6	7	8	9	10	GOOD RUN

NUTRITION

BEFORE	DURING	AFTER

RUN 2

TIME/DISTANCE	WEATHER

COMMENTS

BAD RUN	1	2	3	4	5	6	7	8	9	10	GOOD RUN

NUTRITION

BEFORE	DURING	AFTER

SPEEDWORK

1

TIME/DISTANCE	REPS	RECOVERY

2

TIME/DISTANCE	REPS	RECOVERY

MOOD	LOW	1	2	3	4	5	6	7	8	9	10	HIGH
ENERGY	LOW	1	2	3	4	5	6	7	8	9	10	HIGH
NUTRITION		1	2	3	4	5	6	7	8	9	10	
WATER 8oz		1	2	3	4	5	6	7	8	9	10	

SLEEP DIARY

WEEK 9 | DAY 2 | DATE

RUN 1

TIME/DISTANCE	WEATHER

COMMENTS

BAD RUN 1 2 3 4 5 6 7 8 9 10 GOOD RUN

NUTRITION

BEFORE	DURING	AFTER

RUN 2

TIME/DISTANCE	WEATHER

COMMENTS

BAD RUN 1 2 3 4 5 6 7 8 9 10 GOOD RUN

NUTRITION

BEFORE	DURING	AFTER

SPEEDWORK

1

TIME/DISTANCE	REPS	RECOVERY

2

TIME/DISTANCE	REPS	RECOVERY

MOOD	LOW	1	2	3	4	5	6	7	8	9	10	HIGH
ENERGY	LOW	1	2	3	4	5	6	7	8	9	10	HIGH
NUTRITION		1	2	3	4	5	6	7	8	9	10	
WATER 8oz		1	2	3	4	5	6	7	8	9	10	

SLEEP DIARY

RUN JOURNAL

WEEK 9 | DAY 3 | DATE

RUN
1

TIME/DISTANCE	WEATHER

COMMENTS

BAD RUN 1 2 3 4 5 6 7 8 9 10 GOOD RUN

NUTRITION

BEFORE	DURING	AFTER

RUN
2

TIME/DISTANCE	WEATHER

COMMENTS

BAD RUN 1 2 3 4 5 6 7 8 9 10 GOOD RUN

NUTRITION

BEFORE	DURING	AFTER

SPEEDWORK

1

TIME/DISTANCE	REPS	RECOVERY

2

TIME/DISTANCE	REPS	RECOVERY

MOOD	LOW	1	2	3	4	5	6	7	8	9	10	HIGH
ENERGY	LOW	1	2	3	4	5	6	7	8	9	10	HIGH
NUTRITION		1	2	3	4	5	6	7	8	9	10	
WATER 8oz		1	2	3	4	5	6	7	8	9	10	

SLEEP DIARY

WEEK 9 | DAY 4 | DATE

RUN

1

TIME/DISTANCE	WEATHER

COMMENTS

BAD RUN 1 2 3 4 5 6 7 8 9 10 GOOD RUN

NUTRITION

BEFORE	DURING	AFTER

RUN

2

TIME/DISTANCE	WEATHER

COMMENTS

BAD RUN 1 2 3 4 5 6 7 8 9 10 GOOD RUN

NUTRITION

BEFORE	DURING	AFTER

SPEEDWORK

1

TIME/DISTANCE	REPS	RECOVERY

2

TIME/DISTANCE	REPS	RECOVERY

MOOD	LOW	1	2	3	4	5	6	7	8	9	10	HIGH
ENERGY	LOW	1	2	3	4	5	6	7	8	9	10	HIGH
NUTRITION		1	2	3	4	5	6	7	8	9	10	
WATER 8oz		1	2	3	4	5	6	7	8	9	10	

SLEEP DIARY

RUN JOURNAL

WEEK 9 | DAY 5 | DATE

RUN 1

TIME/DISTANCE	WEATHER

COMMENTS

BAD RUN 1 2 3 4 5 6 7 8 9 10 GOOD RUN

NUTRITION

BEFORE	DURING	AFTER

RUN 2

TIME/DISTANCE	WEATHER

COMMENTS

BAD RUN 1 2 3 4 5 6 7 8 9 10 GOOD RUN

NUTRITION

BEFORE	DURING	AFTER

SPEEDWORK

1

TIME/DISTANCE	REPS	RECOVERY

2

TIME/DISTANCE	REPS	RECOVERY

MOOD	LOW	1	2	3	4	5	6	7	8	9	10	HIGH
ENERGY	LOW	1	2	3	4	5	6	7	8	9	10	HIGH
NUTRITION		1	2	3	4	5	6	7	8	9	10	
WATER 8oz		1	2	3	4	5	6	7	8	9	10	

SLEEP DIARY

WEEK 9 | DAY 6 | DATE

RUN 1

TIME/DISTANCE	WEATHER

COMMENTS

BAD RUN	1	2	3	4	5	6	7	8	9	10	GOOD RUN

NUTRITION

BEFORE	DURING	AFTER

RUN 2

TIME/DISTANCE	WEATHER

COMMENTS

BAD RUN	1	2	3	4	5	6	7	8	9	10	GOOD RUN

NUTRITION

BEFORE	DURING	AFTER

SPEEDWORK

1

TIME/DISTANCE	REPS	RECOVERY

2

TIME/DISTANCE	REPS	RECOVERY

MOOD	LOW	1	2	3	4	5	6	7	8	9	10	HIGH
ENERGY	LOW	1	2	3	4	5	6	7	8	9	10	HIGH
NUTRITION		1	2	3	4	5	6	7	8	9	10	
WATER 8oz		1	2	3	4	5	6	7	8	9	10	

SLEEP DIARY

RUN JOURNAL

WEEK 9 | DAY 7 | DATE

RUN

1

TIME/DISTANCE	WEATHER

COMMENTS

BAD RUN 1 2 3 4 5 6 7 8 9 10 GOOD RUN

NUTRITION

BEFORE	DURING	AFTER

RUN

2

TIME/DISTANCE	WEATHER

COMMENTS

BAD RUN 1 2 3 4 5 6 7 8 9 10 GOOD RUN

NUTRITION

BEFORE	DURING	AFTER

SPEEDWORK

1

TIME/DISTANCE	REPS	RECOVERY

2

TIME/DISTANCE	REPS	RECOVERY

MOOD	LOW	1	2	3	4	5	6	7	8	9	10	HIGH
ENERGY	LOW	1	2	3	4	5	6	7	8	9	10	HIGH
NUTRITION		1	2	3	4	5	6	7	8	9	10	
WATER 8oz		1	2	3	4	5	6	7	8	9	10	

SLEEP DIARY

WEEK 9 SUMMARY

DATE

GOALS MET

GOALS EXCEEDED

NEXT WEEK

RUNNING NOTES

SPEEDWORK NOTES

REFUELING NOTES

	Calories consumed	
MINUS	Calories Used	
EQUALS	Net Calories	
	BMR	
	net calories deficit	

VITAMINS	DOSAGE	QTY

MOOD

1 2 3 4 5 6 7 8 9 10

ENERGY LEVEL

1 2 3 4 5 6 7 8 9 10

Journal

RUN JOURNAL

WEEK 10 | DAY 1 | DATE

RUN 1

TIME/DISTANCE	WEATHER

COMMENTS

BAD RUN 1 2 3 4 5 6 7 8 9 10 GOOD RUN

NUTRITION

BEFORE	DURING	AFTER

RUN 2

TIME/DISTANCE	WEATHER

COMMENTS

BAD RUN 1 2 3 4 5 6 7 8 9 10 GOOD RUN

NUTRITION

BEFORE	DURING	AFTER

SPEEDWORK

1

TIME/DISTANCE	REPS	RECOVERY

2

TIME/DISTANCE	REPS	RECOVERY

MOOD	LOW	1	2	3	4	5	6	7	8	9	10	HIGH
ENERGY	LOW	1	2	3	4	5	6	7	8	9	10	HIGH
NUTRITION		1	2	3	4	5	6	7	8	9	10	
WATER 8oz		1	2	3	4	5	6	7	8	9	10	

SLEEP DIARY

WEEK 10 | DAY 2 | DATE

RUN 1

TIME/DISTANCE	WEATHER

COMMENTS

BAD RUN 1 2 3 4 5 6 7 8 9 10 GOOD RUN

NUTRITION

BEFORE	DURING	AFTER

RUN 2

TIME/DISTANCE	WEATHER

COMMENTS

BAD RUN 1 2 3 4 5 6 7 8 9 10 GOOD RUN

NUTRITION

BEFORE	DURING	AFTER

SPEEDWORK

1

TIME/DISTANCE	REPS	RECOVERY

2

TIME/DISTANCE	REPS	RECOVERY

MOOD	LOW	1	2	3	4	5	6	7	8	9	10	HIGH
ENERGY	LOW	1	2	3	4	5	6	7	8	9	10	HIGH
NUTRITION		1	2	3	4	5	6	7	8	9	10	
WATER 8oz		1	2	3	4	5	6	7	8	9	10	

SLEEP DIARY

RUN JOURNAL

WEEK 10 | DAY 3 | DATE

RUN 1

TIME/DISTANCE	WEATHER

COMMENTS

BAD RUN 1 2 3 4 5 6 7 8 9 10 GOOD RUN

NUTRITION

BEFORE	DURING	AFTER

RUN 2

TIME/DISTANCE	WEATHER

COMMENTS

BAD RUN 1 2 3 4 5 6 7 8 9 10 GOOD RUN

NUTRITION

BEFORE	DURING	AFTER

SPEEDWORK

1

TIME/DISTANCE	REPS	RECOVERY

2

TIME/DISTANCE	REPS	RECOVERY

MOOD	LOW	1	2	3	4	5	6	7	8	9	10	HIGH
ENERGY	LOW	1	2	3	4	5	6	7	8	9	10	HIGH
NUTRITION		1	2	3	4	5	6	7	8	9	10	
WATER 8oz		1	2	3	4	5	6	7	8	9	10	

SLEEP DIARY

WEEK 10 | DAY 4 | DATE

RUN 1

TIME/DISTANCE | WEATHER

COMMENTS

BAD RUN 1 2 3 4 5 6 7 8 9 10 GOOD RUN

NUTRITION

BEFORE | DURING | AFTER

RUN 2

TIME/DISTANCE | WEATHER

COMMENTS

BAD RUN 1 2 3 4 5 6 7 8 9 10 GOOD RUN

NUTRITION

BEFORE | DURING | AFTER

SPEEDWORK

1

TIME/DISTANCE | REPS | RECOVERY

2

TIME/DISTANCE | REPS | RECOVERY

MOOD LOW 1 2 3 4 5 6 7 8 9 10 HIGH

ENERGY LOW 1 2 3 4 5 6 7 8 9 10 HIGH

NUTRITION 1 2 3 4 5 6 7 8 9 10

WATER 8oz 1 2 3 4 5 6 7 8 9 10

SLEEP DIARY

RUN JOURNAL

WEEK 10 | DAY 5 | DATE

RUN

1

TIME/DISTANCE	WEATHER

COMMENTS

BAD RUN	1	2	3	4	5	6	7	8	9	10	GOOD RUN

NUTRITION

BEFORE	DURING	AFTER

RUN

2

TIME/DISTANCE	WEATHER

COMMENTS

BAD RUN	1	2	3	4	5	6	7	8	9	10	GOOD RUN

NUTRITION

BEFORE	DURING	AFTER

SPEEDWORK

1

TIME/DISTANCE	REPS	RECOVERY

2

TIME/DISTANCE	REPS	RECOVERY

MOOD	LOW	1	2	3	4	5	6	7	8	9	10	HIGH
ENERGY	LOW	1	2	3	4	5	6	7	8	9	10	HIGH
NUTRITION		1	2	3	4	5	6	7	8	9	10	
WATER 8oz		1	2	3	4	5	6	7	8	9	10	

SLEEP DIARY

WEEK 10 | DAY 6 | DATE

RUN

1

TIME/DISTANCE	WEATHER

COMMENTS

BAD RUN 1 2 3 4 5 6 7 8 9 10 GOOD RUN

NUTRITION

BEFORE	DURING	AFTER

RUN

2

TIME/DISTANCE	WEATHER

COMMENTS

BAD RUN 1 2 3 4 5 6 7 8 9 10 GOOD RUN

NUTRITION

BEFORE	DURING	AFTER

SPEEDWORK

1

TIME/DISTANCE	REPS	RECOVERY

2

TIME/DISTANCE	REPS	RECOVERY

MOOD	LOW	1	2	3	4	5	6	7	8	9	10	HIGH
ENERGY	LOW	1	2	3	4	5	6	7	8	9	10	HIGH
NUTRITION		1	2	3	4	5	6	7	8	9	10	
WATER 8oz		1	2	3	4	5	6	7	8	9	10	

SLEEP DIARY

RUN JOURNAL

WEEK 10 | DAY 7 | DATE

RUN 1

TIME/DISTANCE	WEATHER

COMMENTS

BAD RUN 1 2 3 4 5 6 7 8 9 10 GOOD RUN

NUTRITION

BEFORE	DURING	AFTER

RUN 2

TIME/DISTANCE	WEATHER

COMMENTS

BAD RUN 1 2 3 4 5 6 7 8 9 10 GOOD RUN

NUTRITION

BEFORE	DURING	AFTER

SPEEDWORK

1

TIME/DISTANCE	REPS	RECOVERY

2

TIME/DISTANCE	REPS	RECOVERY

MOOD	LOW	1	2	3	4	5	6	7	8	9	10	HIGH
ENERGY	LOW	1	2	3	4	5	6	7	8	9	10	HIGH
NUTRITION		1	2	3	4	5	6	7	8	9	10	
WATER 8oz		1	2	3	4	5	6	7	8	9	10	

SLEEP DIARY

WEEK 10 SUMMARY

DATE

GOALS MET

GOALS EXCEEDED

NEXT WEEK

RUNNING NOTES

SPEEDWORK NOTES

REFUELING NOTES

Calories consumed	
MINUS Calories Used	
EQUALS Net Calories	
BMR	
net calories deficit	

MOOD

1 2 3 4 5 6 7 8 9 10

ENERGY LEVEL

1 2 3 4 5 6 7 8 9 10

VITAMINS	DOSAGE	QTY

Journal

RUN JOURNAL

WEEK 11 | DAY 1 | DATE

RUN

1

TIME/DISTANCE	WEATHER

COMMENTS

BAD RUN 1 2 3 4 5 6 7 8 9 10 GOOD RUN

NUTRITION

BEFORE	DURING	AFTER

RUN

2

TIME/DISTANCE	WEATHER

COMMENTS

BAD RUN 1 2 3 4 5 6 7 8 9 10 GOOD RUN

NUTRITION

BEFORE	DURING	AFTER

SPEEDWORK

1

TIME/DISTANCE	REPS	RECOVERY

2

TIME/DISTANCE	REPS	RECOVERY

MOOD	LOW	1	2	3	4	5	6	7	8	9	10	HIGH
ENERGY	LOW	1	2	3	4	5	6	7	8	9	10	HIGH
NUTRITION		1	2	3	4	5	6	7	8	9	10	
WATER 8oz		1	2	3	4	5	6	7	8	9	10	

SLEEP DIARY

WEEK 11 | DAY 2 | DATE

RUN 1

TIME/DISTANCE	WEATHER

COMMENTS

BAD RUN 1 2 3 4 5 6 7 8 9 10 GOOD RUN

NUTRITION

BEFORE	DURING	AFTER

RUN 2

TIME/DISTANCE	WEATHER

COMMENTS

BAD RUN 1 2 3 4 5 6 7 8 9 10 GOOD RUN

NUTRITION

BEFORE	DURING	AFTER

SPEEDWORK

1

TIME/DISTANCE	REPS	RECOVERY

2

TIME/DISTANCE	REPS	RECOVERY

MOOD	LOW	1	2	3	4	5	6	7	8	9	10	HIGH
ENERGY	LOW	1	2	3	4	5	6	7	8	9	10	HIGH
NUTRITION		1	2	3	4	5	6	7	8	9	10	
WATER 8oz		1	2	3	4	5	6	7	8	9	10	

SLEEP DIARY

RUN JOURNAL

WEEK 11 | DAY 3 | DATE

RUN 1

TIME/DISTANCE	WEATHER

COMMENTS

BAD RUN 1 2 3 4 5 6 7 8 9 10 GOOD RUN

NUTRITION

BEFORE	DURING	AFTER

RUN 2

TIME/DISTANCE	WEATHER

COMMENTS

BAD RUN 1 2 3 4 5 6 7 8 9 10 GOOD RUN

NUTRITION

BEFORE	DURING	AFTER

SPEEDWORK

1

TIME/DISTANCE	REPS	RECOVERY

2

TIME/DISTANCE	REPS	RECOVERY

MOOD	LOW	1	2	3	4	5	6	7	8	9	10	HIGH
ENERGY	LOW	1	2	3	4	5	6	7	8	9	10	HIGH
NUTRITION		1	2	3	4	5	6	7	8	9	10	
WATER 8oz		1	2	3	4	5	6	7	8	9	10	

SLEEP DIARY

WEEK 11 | DAY 4 | DATE

RUN 1

TIME/DISTANCE	WEATHER

COMMENTS

BAD RUN 1 2 3 4 5 6 7 8 9 10 GOOD RUN

NUTRITION

BEFORE	DURING	AFTER

RUN 2

TIME/DISTANCE	WEATHER

COMMENTS

BAD RUN 1 2 3 4 5 6 7 8 9 10 GOOD RUN

NUTRITION

BEFORE	DURING	AFTER

SPEEDWORK

1

TIME/DISTANCE	REPS	RECOVERY

2

TIME/DISTANCE	REPS	RECOVERY

MOOD	LOW	1	2	3	4	5	6	7	8	9	10	HIGH
ENERGY	LOW	1	2	3	4	5	6	7	8	9	10	HIGH
NUTRITION		1	2	3	4	5	6	7	8	9	10	
WATER 8oz		1	2	3	4	5	6	7	8	9	10	

SLEEP DIARY

RUN JOURNAL

WEEK 11 | DAY 5 | DATE

RUN 1

TIME/DISTANCE	WEATHER

COMMENTS

BAD RUN 1 2 3 4 5 6 7 8 9 10 GOOD RUN

NUTRITION

BEFORE	DURING	AFTER

RUN 2

TIME/DISTANCE	WEATHER

COMMENTS

BAD RUN 1 2 3 4 5 6 7 8 9 10 GOOD RUN

NUTRITION

BEFORE	DURING	AFTER

SPEEDWORK

1

TIME/DISTANCE	REPS	RECOVERY

2

TIME/DISTANCE	REPS	RECOVERY

MOOD	LOW	1	2	3	4	5	6	7	8	9	10	HIGH
ENERGY	LOW	1	2	3	4	5	6	7	8	9	10	HIGH
NUTRITION		1	2	3	4	5	6	7	8	9	10	
WATER 8oz		1	2	3	4	5	6	7	8	9	10	

SLEEP DIARY

WEEK 11 | DAY 6 | DATE

RUN 1

TIME/DISTANCE	WEATHER

COMMENTS

BAD RUN 1 2 3 4 5 6 7 8 9 10 GOOD RUN

NUTRITION

BEFORE	DURING	AFTER

RUN 2

TIME/DISTANCE	WEATHER

COMMENTS

BAD RUN 1 2 3 4 5 6 7 8 9 10 GOOD RUN

NUTRITION

BEFORE	DURING	AFTER

SPEEDWORK

1

TIME/DISTANCE	REPS	RECOVERY

2

TIME/DISTANCE	REPS	RECOVERY

MOOD	LOW	1	2	3	4	5	6	7	8	9	10	HIGH
ENERGY	LOW	1	2	3	4	5	6	7	8	9	10	HIGH
NUTRITION		1	2	3	4	5	6	7	8	9	10	
WATER 8oz		1	2	3	4	5	6	7	8	9	10	

SLEEP DIARY

RUN JOURNAL

WEEK 11 | DAY 7 | DATE

RUN 1

TIME/DISTANCE	WEATHER

COMMENTS

BAD RUN 1 2 3 4 5 6 7 8 9 10 GOOD RUN

NUTRITION

BEFORE	DURING	AFTER

RUN 2

TIME/DISTANCE	WEATHER

COMMENTS

BAD RUN 1 2 3 4 5 6 7 8 9 10 GOOD RUN

NUTRITION

BEFORE	DURING	AFTER

SPEEDWORK

1

TIME/DISTANCE	REPS	RECOVERY

2

TIME/DISTANCE	REPS	RECOVERY

MOOD	LOW	1	2	3	4	5	6	7	8	9	10	HIGH
ENERGY	LOW	1	2	3	4	5	6	7	8	9	10	HIGH
NUTRITION		1	2	3	4	5	6	7	8	9	10	
WATER 8oz		1	2	3	4	5	6	7	8	9	10	

SLEEP DIARY

WEEK 11 SUMMARY

DATE

GOALS MET

GOALS EXCEEDED

NEXT WEEK

RUNNING NOTES

SPEEDWORK NOTES

REFUELING NOTES

	Calories consumed	
MINUS	Calories Used	
EQUALS	Net Calories	
	BMR	
	net calories deficit	

VITAMINS	DOSAGE	QTY

MOOD

1 2 3 4 5 6 7 8 9 10

ENERGY LEVEL

1 2 3 4 5 6 7 8 9 10

Journal

RUN JOURNAL

WEEK 12 | DAY 1 | DATE

RUN 1

TIME/DISTANCE	WEATHER

COMMENTS

BAD RUN 1 2 3 4 5 6 7 8 9 10 GOOD RUN

NUTRITION

BEFORE	DURING	AFTER

RUN 2

TIME/DISTANCE	WEATHER

COMMENTS

BAD RUN 1 2 3 4 5 6 7 8 9 10 GOOD RUN

NUTRITION

BEFORE	DURING	AFTER

SPEEDWORK

1

TIME/DISTANCE	REPS	RECOVERY

2

TIME/DISTANCE	REPS	RECOVERY

MOOD	LOW	1	2	3	4	5	6	7	8	9	10	HIGH
ENERGY	LOW	1	2	3	4	5	6	7	8	9	10	HIGH
NUTRITION		1	2	3	4	5	6	7	8	9	10	
WATER 8oz		1	2	3	4	5	6	7	8	9	10	

SLEEP DIARY

WEEK 12 | DAY 2 | DATE

RUN 1

TIME/DISTANCE | WEATHER

COMMENTS

BAD RUN 1 2 3 4 5 6 7 8 9 10 GOOD RUN

NUTRITION

BEFORE | DURING | AFTER

RUN 2

TIME/DISTANCE | WEATHER

COMMENTS

BAD RUN 1 2 3 4 5 6 7 8 9 10 GOOD RUN

NUTRITION

BEFORE | DURING | AFTER

SPEEDWORK

1

TIME/DISTANCE	REPS	RECOVERY

2

TIME/DISTANCE	REPS	RECOVERY

MOOD	LOW	1	2	3	4	5	6	7	8	9	10	HIGH
ENERGY	LOW	1	2	3	4	5	6	7	8	9	10	HIGH
NUTRITION		1	2	3	4	5	6	7	8	9	10	
WATER 8oz		1	2	3	4	5	6	7	8	9	10	

SLEEP DIARY

RUN JOURNAL

WEEK 12 | DAY 3 | DATE

RUN 1

TIME/DISTANCE	WEATHER

COMMENTS

BAD RUN 1 2 3 4 5 6 7 8 9 10 GOOD RUN

NUTRITION

BEFORE	DURING	AFTER

RUN 2

TIME/DISTANCE	WEATHER

COMMENTS

BAD RUN 1 2 3 4 5 6 7 8 9 10 GOOD RUN

NUTRITION

BEFORE	DURING	AFTER

SPEEDWORK

1

TIME/DISTANCE	REPS	RECOVERY

2

TIME/DISTANCE	REPS	RECOVERY

MOOD	LOW	1	2	3	4	5	6	7	8	9	10	HIGH
ENERGY	LOW	1	2	3	4	5	6	7	8	9	10	HIGH
NUTRITION		1	2	3	4	5	6	7	8	9	10	
WATER 8oz		1	2	3	4	5	6	7	8	9	10	

SLEEP DIARY

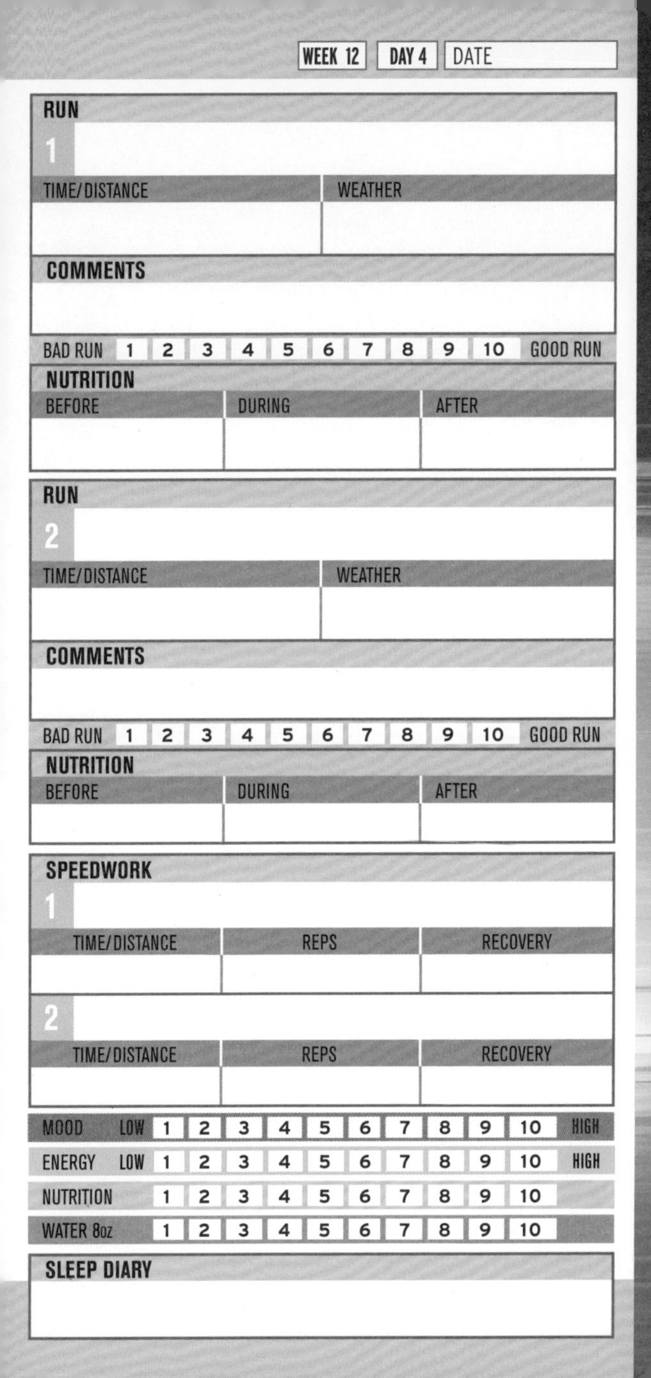

WEEK 12 | DAY 4 | DATE

RUN 1

TIME/DISTANCE	WEATHER

COMMENTS

BAD RUN 1 2 3 4 5 6 7 8 9 10 GOOD RUN

NUTRITION

BEFORE	DURING	AFTER

RUN 2

TIME/DISTANCE	WEATHER

COMMENTS

BAD RUN 1 2 3 4 5 6 7 8 9 10 GOOD RUN

NUTRITION

BEFORE	DURING	AFTER

SPEEDWORK

1

TIME/DISTANCE	REPS	RECOVERY

2

TIME/DISTANCE	REPS	RECOVERY

MOOD	LOW	1	2	3	4	5	6	7	8	9	10	HIGH
ENERGY	LOW	1	2	3	4	5	6	7	8	9	10	HIGH
NUTRITION		1	2	3	4	5	6	7	8	9	10	
WATER 8oz		1	2	3	4	5	6	7	8	9	10	

SLEEP DIARY

RUN JOURNAL

WEEK 12 | DAY 5 | DATE

RUN 1

TIME/DISTANCE	WEATHER

COMMENTS

BAD RUN 1 2 3 4 5 6 7 8 9 10 GOOD RUN

NUTRITION

BEFORE	DURING	AFTER

RUN 2

TIME/DISTANCE	WEATHER

COMMENTS

BAD RUN 1 2 3 4 5 6 7 8 9 10 GOOD RUN

NUTRITION

BEFORE	DURING	AFTER

SPEEDWORK

1

TIME/DISTANCE	REPS	RECOVERY

2

TIME/DISTANCE	REPS	RECOVERY

MOOD LOW 1 2 3 4 5 6 7 8 9 10 HIGH

ENERGY LOW 1 2 3 4 5 6 7 8 9 10 HIGH

NUTRITION 1 2 3 4 5 6 7 8 9 10

WATER 8oz 1 2 3 4 5 6 7 8 9 10

SLEEP DIARY

WEEK 12 | DAY 6 | DATE

RUN 1

TIME/DISTANCE	WEATHER

COMMENTS

BAD RUN 1 2 3 4 5 6 7 8 9 10 GOOD RUN

NUTRITION

BEFORE	DURING	AFTER

RUN 2

TIME/DISTANCE	WEATHER

COMMENTS

BAD RUN 1 2 3 4 5 6 7 8 9 10 GOOD RUN

NUTRITION

BEFORE	DURING	AFTER

SPEEDWORK

1

TIME/DISTANCE	REPS	RECOVERY

2

TIME/DISTANCE	REPS	RECOVERY

MOOD	LOW	1	2	3	4	5	6	7	8	9	10	HIGH
ENERGY	LOW	1	2	3	4	5	6	7	8	9	10	HIGH
NUTRITION		1	2	3	4	5	6	7	8	9	10	
WATER 8oz		1	2	3	4	5	6	7	8	9	10	

SLEEP DIARY

RUN JOURNAL

WEEK 12 | DAY 7 | DATE

RUN 1

TIME/DISTANCE	WEATHER

COMMENTS

BAD RUN 1 2 3 4 5 6 7 8 9 10 GOOD RUN

NUTRITION

BEFORE	DURING	AFTER

RUN 2

TIME/DISTANCE	WEATHER

COMMENTS

BAD RUN 1 2 3 4 5 6 7 8 9 10 GOOD RUN

NUTRITION

BEFORE	DURING	AFTER

SPEEDWORK

1

TIME/DISTANCE	REPS	RECOVERY

2

TIME/DISTANCE	REPS	RECOVERY

MOOD LOW 1 2 3 4 5 6 7 8 9 10 HIGH

ENERGY LOW 1 2 3 4 5 6 7 8 9 10 HIGH

NUTRITION 1 2 3 4 5 6 7 8 9 10

WATER 8oz 1 2 3 4 5 6 7 8 9 10

SLEEP DIARY

WEEK 12 SUMMARY

DATE

GOALS MET	
GOALS EXCEEDED	
NEXT WEEK	

RUNNING NOTES

SPEEDWORK NOTES

REFUELING NOTES

	Calories consumed	
MINUS	Calories Used	
EQUALS	Net Calories	
	BMR	
	net calories deficit	

MOOD

1 2 3 4 5 6 7 8 9 10

ENERGY LEVEL

1 2 3 4 5 6 7 8 9 10

VITAMINS	DOSAGE	QTY

Journal

MONTH 3 SUMMARY

GOALS MET | GOALS EXCEEDED | MAYBE NEXT WEEK

RUNNING NOTES

SPEEDWORK NOTES

MOOD & ENERGY

TOTAL
RUNNING SESSIONS

TOTAL
SPEEDWORK SESSIONS

GOALS FOR NEXT MONTH

RUN TRAINING GOALS	SPEED TRAINING GOALS

WINTER RUNNING TIPS

As winter approaches the temperature drops and it starts to get dark earlier and earlier, keeping warm and safe are priorities for winter running. Running thermals, hats and gloves are a must, they are very effective for keeping your body heat in. Making sure that you're visible to traffic is essential in the dark mornings and evenings. When you get in from training, try to get in a hot shower as soon as you can to get some heat back in your body.

RUN JOURNAL

WEEK 13 | DAY 1 | DATE

RUN 1

TIME/DISTANCE	WEATHER

COMMENTS

BAD RUN	1	2	3	4	5	6	7	8	9	10	GOOD RUN

NUTRITION

BEFORE	DURING	AFTER

RUN 2

TIME/DISTANCE	WEATHER

COMMENTS

BAD RUN	1	2	3	4	5	6	7	8	9	10	GOOD RUN

NUTRITION

BEFORE	DURING	AFTER

SPEEDWORK

1

TIME/DISTANCE	REPS	RECOVERY

2

TIME/DISTANCE	REPS	RECOVERY

MOOD	LOW	1	2	3	4	5	6	7	8	9	10	HIGH
ENERGY	LOW	1	2	3	4	5	6	7	8	9	10	HIGH
NUTRITION		1	2	3	4	5	6	7	8	9	10	
WATER 8oz		1	2	3	4	5	6	7	8	9	10	

SLEEP DIARY

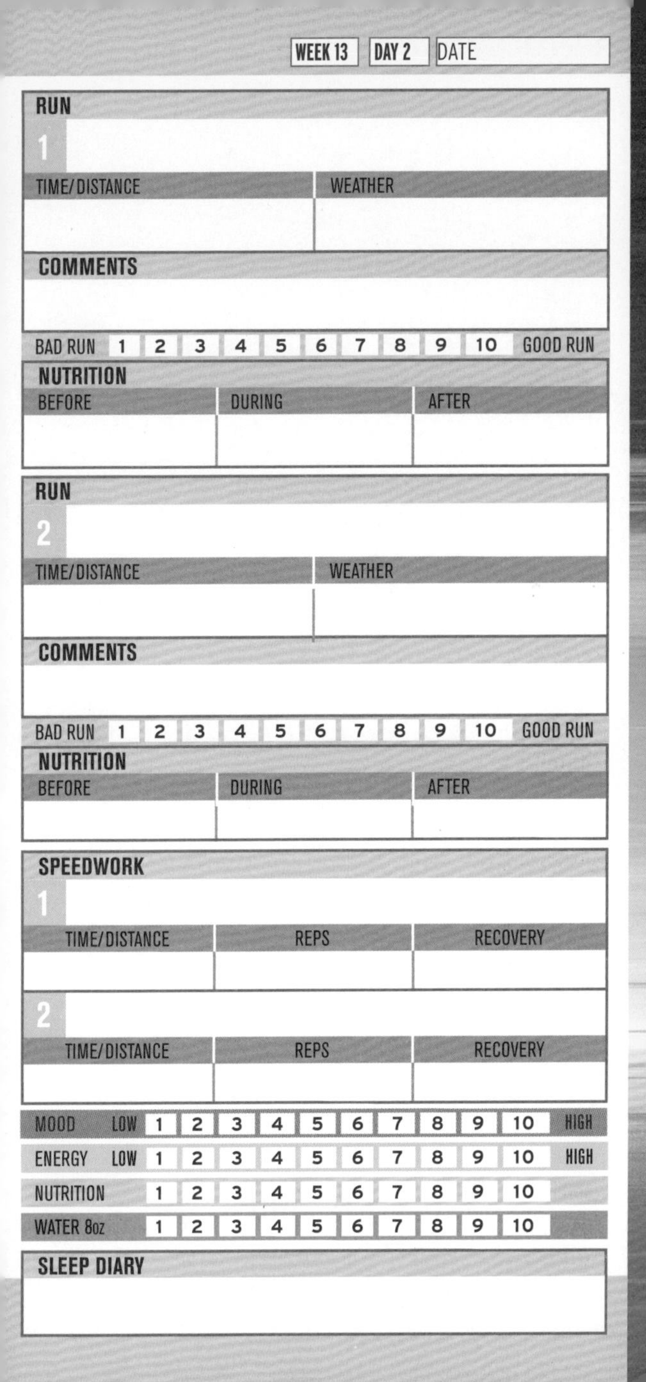

WEEK 13 | DAY 2 | DATE

RUN 1

TIME/DISTANCE	WEATHER

COMMENTS

BAD RUN 1 2 3 4 5 6 7 8 9 10 GOOD RUN

NUTRITION

BEFORE	DURING	AFTER

RUN 2

TIME/DISTANCE	WEATHER

COMMENTS

BAD RUN 1 2 3 4 5 6 7 8 9 10 GOOD RUN

NUTRITION

BEFORE	DURING	AFTER

SPEEDWORK

1

TIME/DISTANCE	REPS	RECOVERY

2

TIME/DISTANCE	REPS	RECOVERY

MOOD LOW 1 2 3 4 5 6 7 8 9 10 HIGH

ENERGY LOW 1 2 3 4 5 6 7 8 9 10 HIGH

NUTRITION 1 2 3 4 5 6 7 8 9 10

WATER 8oz 1 2 3 4 5 6 7 8 9 10

SLEEP DIARY

RUN JOURNAL

WEEK 13 | DAY 3 | DATE

RUN 1

TIME/DISTANCE	WEATHER

COMMENTS

BAD RUN 1 2 3 4 5 6 7 8 9 10 GOOD RUN

NUTRITION

BEFORE	DURING	AFTER

RUN 2

TIME/DISTANCE	WEATHER

COMMENTS

BAD RUN 1 2 3 4 5 6 7 8 9 10 GOOD RUN

NUTRITION

BEFORE	DURING	AFTER

SPEEDWORK

1

TIME/DISTANCE	REPS	RECOVERY

2

TIME/DISTANCE	REPS	RECOVERY

MOOD	LOW	1	2	3	4	5	6	7	8	9	10	HIGH
ENERGY	LOW	1	2	3	4	5	6	7	8	9	10	HIGH
NUTRITION		1	2	3	4	5	6	7	8	9	10	
WATER 8oz		1	2	3	4	5	6	7	8	9	10	

SLEEP DIARY

WEEK 13 | DAY 4 | DATE

RUN

1

TIME/DISTANCE	WEATHER

COMMENTS

BAD RUN 1 2 3 4 5 6 7 8 9 10 GOOD RUN

NUTRITION

BEFORE	DURING	AFTER

RUN

2

TIME/DISTANCE	WEATHER

COMMENTS

BAD RUN 1 2 3 4 5 6 7 8 9 10 GOOD RUN

NUTRITION

BEFORE	DURING	AFTER

SPEEDWORK

1

TIME/DISTANCE	REPS	RECOVERY

2

TIME/DISTANCE	REPS	RECOVERY

MOOD	LOW	1	2	3	4	5	6	7	8	9	10	HIGH
ENERGY	LOW	1	2	3	4	5	6	7	8	9	10	HIGH
NUTRITION		1	2	3	4	5	6	7	8	9	10	
WATER 8oz		1	2	3	4	5	6	7	8	9	10	

SLEEP DIARY

RUN JOURNAL

WEEK 13 | DAY 5 | DATE

RUN 1

TIME/DISTANCE	WEATHER

COMMENTS

BAD RUN 1 2 3 4 5 6 7 8 9 10 GOOD RUN

NUTRITION

BEFORE	DURING	AFTER

RUN 2

TIME/DISTANCE	WEATHER

COMMENTS

BAD RUN 1 2 3 4 5 6 7 8 9 10 GOOD RUN

NUTRITION

BEFORE	DURING	AFTER

SPEEDWORK

1

TIME/DISTANCE	REPS	RECOVERY

2

TIME/DISTANCE	REPS	RECOVERY

MOOD	LOW	1	2	3	4	5	6	7	8	9	10	HIGH
ENERGY	LOW	1	2	3	4	5	6	7	8	9	10	HIGH
NUTRITION		1	2	3	4	5	6	7	8	9	10	
WATER 8oz		1	2	3	4	5	6	7	8	9	10	

SLEEP DIARY

WEEK 13 | DAY 6 | DATE

RUN 1

TIME/DISTANCE	WEATHER

COMMENTS

BAD RUN 1 2 3 4 5 6 7 8 9 10 GOOD RUN

NUTRITION

BEFORE	DURING	AFTER

RUN 2

TIME/DISTANCE	WEATHER

COMMENTS

BAD RUN 1 2 3 4 5 6 7 8 9 10 GOOD RUN

NUTRITION

BEFORE	DURING	AFTER

SPEEDWORK

1

TIME/DISTANCE	REPS	RECOVERY

2

TIME/DISTANCE	REPS	RECOVERY

MOOD	LOW	1	2	3	4	5	6	7	8	9	10	HIGH
ENERGY	LOW	1	2	3	4	5	6	7	8	9	10	HIGH
NUTRITION		1	2	3	4	5	6	7	8	9	10	
WATER 8oz		1	2	3	4	5	6	7	8	9	10	

SLEEP DIARY

RUN JOURNAL

WEEK 13 | DAY 7 | DATE

RUN

1

TIME/DISTANCE	WEATHER

COMMENTS

BAD RUN 1 2 3 4 5 6 7 8 9 10 GOOD RUN

NUTRITION

BEFORE	DURING	AFTER

RUN

2

TIME/DISTANCE	WEATHER

COMMENTS

BAD RUN 1 2 3 4 5 6 7 8 9 10 GOOD RUN

NUTRITION

BEFORE	DURING	AFTER

SPEEDWORK

1

TIME/DISTANCE	REPS	RECOVERY

2

TIME/DISTANCE	REPS	RECOVERY

MOOD	LOW	1	2	3	4	5	6	7	8	9	10	HIGH
ENERGY	LOW	1	2	3	4	5	6	7	8	9	10	HIGH
NUTRITION		1	2	3	4	5	6	7	8	9	10	
WATER 8oz		1	2	3	4	5	6	7	8	9	10	

SLEEP DIARY

WEEK 13 SUMMARY

DATE

GOALS MET

GOALS EXCEEDED

NEXT WEEK

RUNNING NOTES

SPEEDWORK NOTES

REFUELING NOTES

	Calories consumed	
MINUS	Calories Used	
EQUALS	Net Calories	
	BMR	
	net calories deficit	

MOOD

1 2 3 4 5 6 7 8 9 10

ENERGY LEVEL

1 2 3 4 5 6 7 8 9 10

VITAMINS	DOSAGE	QTY

Journal

RUN JOURNAL

WEEK 14 | DAY 1 | DATE

RUN

1

TIME/DISTANCE	WEATHER

COMMENTS

BAD RUN 1 2 3 4 5 6 7 8 9 10 GOOD RUN

NUTRITION

BEFORE	DURING	AFTER

RUN

2

TIME/DISTANCE	WEATHER

COMMENTS

BAD RUN 1 2 3 4 5 6 7 8 9 10 GOOD RUN

NUTRITION

BEFORE	DURING	AFTER

SPEEDWORK

1

TIME/DISTANCE	REPS	RECOVERY

2

TIME/DISTANCE	REPS	RECOVERY

MOOD	LOW	1	2	3	4	5	6	7	8	9	10	HIGH
ENERGY	LOW	1	2	3	4	5	6	7	8	9	10	HIGH
NUTRITION		1	2	3	4	5	6	7	8	9	10	
WATER 8oz		1	2	3	4	5	6	7	8	9	10	

SLEEP DIARY

WEEK 14 | DAY 2 | DATE

RUN 1

TIME/DISTANCE	WEATHER

COMMENTS

BAD RUN 1 2 3 4 5 6 7 8 9 10 GOOD RUN

NUTRITION

BEFORE	DURING	AFTER

RUN 2

TIME/DISTANCE	WEATHER

COMMENTS

BAD RUN 1 2 3 4 5 6 7 8 9 10 GOOD RUN

NUTRITION

BEFORE	DURING	AFTER

SPEEDWORK

1

TIME/DISTANCE	REPS	RECOVERY

2

TIME/DISTANCE	REPS	RECOVERY

MOOD	LOW	1	2	3	4	5	6	7	8	9	10	HIGH
ENERGY	LOW	1	2	3	4	5	6	7	8	9	10	HIGH
NUTRITION		1	2	3	4	5	6	7	8	9	10	
WATER 8oz		1	2	3	4	5	6	7	8	9	10	

SLEEP DIARY

RUN JOURNAL

WEEK 14 | DAY 3 | DATE

RUN 1

TIME/DISTANCE	WEATHER

COMMENTS

BAD RUN 1 2 3 4 5 6 7 8 9 10 GOOD RUN

NUTRITION

BEFORE	DURING	AFTER

RUN 2

TIME/DISTANCE	WEATHER

COMMENTS

BAD RUN 1 2 3 4 5 6 7 8 9 10 GOOD RUN

NUTRITION

BEFORE	DURING	AFTER

SPEEDWORK

1

TIME/DISTANCE	REPS	RECOVERY

2

TIME/DISTANCE	REPS	RECOVERY

MOOD	LOW	1	2	3	4	5	6	7	8	9	10	HIGH
ENERGY	LOW	1	2	3	4	5	6	7	8	9	10	HIGH
NUTRITION		1	2	3	4	5	6	7	8	9	10	
WATER 8oz		1	2	3	4	5	6	7	8	9	10	

SLEEP DIARY

WEEK 14 | DAY 4 | DATE

RUN 1

TIME/DISTANCE	WEATHER

COMMENTS

BAD RUN 1 2 3 4 5 6 7 8 9 10 GOOD RUN

NUTRITION

BEFORE	DURING	AFTER

RUN 2

TIME/DISTANCE	WEATHER

COMMENTS

BAD RUN 1 2 3 4 5 6 7 8 9 10 GOOD RUN

NUTRITION

BEFORE	DURING	AFTER

SPEEDWORK

1

TIME/DISTANCE	REPS	RECOVERY

2

TIME/DISTANCE	REPS	RECOVERY

MOOD	LOW	1	2	3	4	5	6	7	8	9	10	HIGH
ENERGY	LOW	1	2	3	4	5	6	7	8	9	10	HIGH
NUTRITION		1	2	3	4	5	6	7	8	9	10	
WATER 8oz		1	2	3	4	5	6	7	8	9	10	

SLEEP DIARY

RUN JOURNAL

WEEK 14 | DAY 5 | DATE

RUN 1

TIME/DISTANCE	WEATHER

COMMENTS

BAD RUN 1 2 3 4 5 6 7 8 9 10 GOOD RUN

NUTRITION

BEFORE	DURING	AFTER

RUN 2

TIME/DISTANCE	WEATHER

COMMENTS

BAD RUN 1 2 3 4 5 6 7 8 9 10 GOOD RUN

NUTRITION

BEFORE	DURING	AFTER

SPEEDWORK

1

TIME/DISTANCE	REPS	RECOVERY

2

TIME/DISTANCE	REPS	RECOVERY

MOOD	LOW	1	2	3	4	5	6	7	8	9	10	HIGH
ENERGY	LOW	1	2	3	4	5	6	7	8	9	10	HIGH
NUTRITION		1	2	3	4	5	6	7	8	9	10	
WATER 8oz		1	2	3	4	5	6	7	8	9	10	

SLEEP DIARY

WEEK 14 | DAY 6 | DATE

RUN 1

TIME/DISTANCE	WEATHER

COMMENTS

BAD RUN	1	2	3	4	5	6	7	8	9	10	GOOD RUN

NUTRITION

BEFORE	DURING	AFTER

RUN 2

TIME/DISTANCE	WEATHER

COMMENTS

BAD RUN	1	2	3	4	5	6	7	8	9	10	GOOD RUN

NUTRITION

BEFORE	DURING	AFTER

SPEEDWORK

1

TIME/DISTANCE	REPS	RECOVERY

2

TIME/DISTANCE	REPS	RECOVERY

MOOD	LOW	1	2	3	4	5	6	7	8	9	10	HIGH
ENERGY	LOW	1	2	3	4	5	6	7	8	9	10	HIGH
NUTRITION		1	2	3	4	5	6	7	8	9	10	
WATER 8oz		1	2	3	4	5	6	7	8	9	10	

SLEEP DIARY

RUN JOURNAL

WEEK 14 | DAY 7 | DATE

RUN 1

TIME/DISTANCE	WEATHER

COMMENTS

BAD RUN 1 2 3 4 5 6 7 8 9 10 GOOD RUN

NUTRITION

BEFORE	DURING	AFTER

RUN 2

TIME/DISTANCE	WEATHER

COMMENTS

BAD RUN 1 2 3 4 5 6 7 8 9 10 GOOD RUN

NUTRITION

BEFORE	DURING	AFTER

SPEEDWORK

1

TIME/DISTANCE	REPS	RECOVERY

2

TIME/DISTANCE	REPS	RECOVERY

MOOD	LOW	1	2	3	4	5	6	7	8	9	10	HIGH
ENERGY	LOW	1	2	3	4	5	6	7	8	9	10	HIGH
NUTRITION		1	2	3	4	5	6	7	8	9	10	
WATER 8oz		1	2	3	4	5	6	7	8	9	10	

SLEEP DIARY

WEEK 14 SUMMARY

DATE

GOALS MET

GOALS EXCEEDED

NEXT WEEK

RUNNING NOTES

SPEEDWORK NOTES

REFUELING NOTES

Calories consumed	
MINUS Calories Used	
EQUALS Net Calories	
BMR	
net calories deficit	

MOOD

1 2 3 4 5 6 7 8 9 10

ENERGY LEVEL

1 2 3 4 5 6 7 8 9 10

VITAMINS	DOSAGE	QTY

Journal

RUN JOURNAL

WEEK 15 | DAY 1 | DATE

RUN 1

TIME/DISTANCE	WEATHER

COMMENTS

BAD RUN 1 2 3 4 5 6 7 8 9 10 GOOD RUN

NUTRITION

BEFORE	DURING	AFTER

RUN 2

TIME/DISTANCE	WEATHER

COMMENTS

BAD RUN 1 2 3 4 5 6 7 8 9 10 GOOD RUN

NUTRITION

BEFORE	DURING	AFTER

SPEEDWORK

1

TIME/DISTANCE	REPS	RECOVERY

2

TIME/DISTANCE	REPS	RECOVERY

MOOD	LOW	1	2	3	4	5	6	7	8	9	10	HIGH
ENERGY	LOW	1	2	3	4	5	6	7	8	9	10	HIGH
NUTRITION		1	2	3	4	5	6	7	8	9	10	
WATER 8oz		1	2	3	4	5	6	7	8	9	10	

SLEEP DIARY

WEEK 15 | DAY 2 | DATE

RUN 1

TIME/DISTANCE	WEATHER

COMMENTS

BAD RUN 1 2 3 4 5 6 7 8 9 10 GOOD RUN

NUTRITION

BEFORE	DURING	AFTER

RUN 2

TIME/DISTANCE	WEATHER

COMMENTS

BAD RUN 1 2 3 4 5 6 7 8 9 10 GOOD RUN

NUTRITION

BEFORE	DURING	AFTER

SPEEDWORK

1

TIME/DISTANCE	REPS	RECOVERY

2

TIME/DISTANCE	REPS	RECOVERY

MOOD	LOW	1	2	3	4	5	6	7	8	9	10	HIGH
ENERGY	LOW	1	2	3	4	5	6	7	8	9	10	HIGH
NUTRITION		1	2	3	4	5	6	7	8	9	10	
WATER 8oz		1	2	3	4	5	6	7	8	9	10	

SLEEP DIARY

RUN JOURNAL

WEEK 15 | DAY 3 | DATE

RUN 1

TIME/DISTANCE	WEATHER

COMMENTS

BAD RUN 1 2 3 4 5 6 7 8 9 10 GOOD RUN

NUTRITION

BEFORE	DURING	AFTER

RUN 2

TIME/DISTANCE	WEATHER

COMMENTS

BAD RUN 1 2 3 4 5 6 7 8 9 10 GOOD RUN

NUTRITION

BEFORE	DURING	AFTER

SPEEDWORK

1

TIME/DISTANCE	REPS	RECOVERY

2

TIME/DISTANCE	REPS	RECOVERY

MOOD	LOW	1	2	3	4	5	6	7	8	9	10	HIGH
ENERGY	LOW	1	2	3	4	5	6	7	8	9	10	HIGH
NUTRITION		1	2	3	4	5	6	7	8	9	10	
WATER 8oz		1	2	3	4	5	6	7	8	9	10	

SLEEP DIARY

RUN

1

TIME/DISTANCE	WEATHER

COMMENTS

BAD RUN 1 2 3 4 5 6 7 8 9 10 GOOD RUN

NUTRITION

BEFORE	DURING	AFTER

RUN

2

TIME/DISTANCE	WEATHER

COMMENTS

BAD RUN 1 2 3 4 5 6 7 8 9 10 GOOD RUN

NUTRITION

BEFORE	DURING	AFTER

SPEEDWORK

1

TIME/DISTANCE	REPS	RECOVERY

2

TIME/DISTANCE	REPS	RECOVERY

MOOD	LOW	1	2	3	4	5	6	7	8	9	10	HIGH
ENERGY	LOW	1	2	3	4	5	6	7	8	9	10	HIGH
NUTRITION		1	2	3	4	5	6	7	8	9	10	
WATER 8oz		1	2	3	4	5	6	7	8	9	10	

SLEEP DIARY

RUN JOURNAL

WEEK 15 | DAY 5 | DATE

RUN 1

TIME/DISTANCE	WEATHER

COMMENTS

BAD RUN 1 2 3 4 5 6 7 8 9 10 GOOD RUN

NUTRITION

BEFORE	DURING	AFTER

RUN 2

TIME/DISTANCE	WEATHER

COMMENTS

BAD RUN 1 2 3 4 5 6 7 8 9 10 GOOD RUN

NUTRITION

BEFORE	DURING	AFTER

SPEEDWORK

1

TIME/DISTANCE	REPS	RECOVERY

2

TIME/DISTANCE	REPS	RECOVERY

MOOD	LOW	1	2	3	4	5	6	7	8	9	10	HIGH
ENERGY	LOW	1	2	3	4	5	6	7	8	9	10	HIGH
NUTRITION		1	2	3	4	5	6	7	8	9	10	
WATER 8oz		1	2	3	4	5	6	7	8	9	10	

SLEEP DIARY

WEEK 15 | DAY 6 | DATE

RUN 1

TIME/DISTANCE	WEATHER

COMMENTS

BAD RUN 1 2 3 4 5 6 7 8 9 10 GOOD RUN

NUTRITION

BEFORE	DURING	AFTER

RUN 2

TIME/DISTANCE	WEATHER

COMMENTS

BAD RUN 1 2 3 4 5 6 7 8 9 10 GOOD RUN

NUTRITION

BEFORE	DURING	AFTER

SPEEDWORK

1

TIME/DISTANCE	REPS	RECOVERY

2

TIME/DISTANCE	REPS	RECOVERY

MOOD	LOW	1	2	3	4	5	6	7	8	9	10	HIGH
ENERGY	LOW	1	2	3	4	5	6	7	8	9	10	HIGH
NUTRITION		1	2	3	4	5	6	7	8	9	10	
WATER 8oz		1	2	3	4	5	6	7	8	9	10	

SLEEP DIARY

RUN JOURNAL

WEEK 15 | DAY 7 | DATE

RUN 1

TIME/DISTANCE	WEATHER

COMMENTS

BAD RUN 1 2 3 4 5 6 7 8 9 10 GOOD RUN

NUTRITION

BEFORE	DURING	AFTER

RUN 2

TIME/DISTANCE	WEATHER

COMMENTS

BAD RUN 1 2 3 4 5 6 7 8 9 10 GOOD RUN

NUTRITION

BEFORE	DURING	AFTER

SPEEDWORK

1

TIME/DISTANCE	REPS	RECOVERY

2

TIME/DISTANCE	REPS	RECOVERY

MOOD	LOW	1	2	3	4	5	6	7	8	9	10	HIGH
ENERGY	LOW	1	2	3	4	5	6	7	8	9	10	HIGH
NUTRITION		1	2	3	4	5	6	7	8	9	10	
WATER 8oz		1	2	3	4	5	6	7	8	9	10	

SLEEP DIARY

WEEK 15 SUMMARY

DATE

GOALS MET

GOALS EXCEEDED

NEXT WEEK

RUNNING NOTES

SPEEDWORK NOTES

REFUELING NOTES

Calories consumed	
MINUS Calories Used	
EQUALS Net Calories	
BMR	
net calories deficit	

VITAMINS	DOSAGE	QTY

MOOD

1 2 3 4 5 6 7 8 9 10

ENERGY LEVEL

1 2 3 4 5 6 7 8 9 10

Journal

RUN JOURNAL

WEEK 16 | DAY 1 | DATE

RUN 1

TIME/DISTANCE | WEATHER

COMMENTS

BAD RUN 1 2 3 4 5 6 7 8 9 10 GOOD RUN

NUTRITION

BEFORE | DURING | AFTER

RUN 2

TIME/DISTANCE | WEATHER

COMMENTS

BAD RUN 1 2 3 4 5 6 7 8 9 10 GOOD RUN

NUTRITION

BEFORE | DURING | AFTER

SPEEDWORK

1

TIME/DISTANCE	REPS	RECOVERY

2

TIME/DISTANCE	REPS	RECOVERY

MOOD	LOW	1	2	3	4	5	6	7	8	9	10	HIGH
ENERGY	LOW	1	2	3	4	5	6	7	8	9	10	HIGH
NUTRITION		1	2	3	4	5	6	7	8	9	10	
WATER 8oz		1	2	3	4	5	6	7	8	9	10	

SLEEP DIARY

WEEK 16 | DAY 2 | DATE

RUN 1

TIME/DISTANCE	WEATHER

COMMENTS

BAD RUN 1 2 3 4 5 6 7 8 9 10 GOOD RUN

NUTRITION

BEFORE	DURING	AFTER

RUN 2

TIME/DISTANCE	WEATHER

COMMENTS

BAD RUN 1 2 3 4 5 6 7 8 9 10 GOOD RUN

NUTRITION

BEFORE	DURING	AFTER

SPEEDWORK

1

TIME/DISTANCE	REPS	RECOVERY

2

TIME/DISTANCE	REPS	RECOVERY

MOOD	LOW	1	2	3	4	5	6	7	8	9	10	HIGH
ENERGY	LOW	1	2	3	4	5	6	7	8	9	10	HIGH
NUTRITION		1	2	3	4	5	6	7	8	9	10	
WATER 8oz		1	2	3	4	5	6	7	8	9	10	

SLEEP DIARY

RUN JOURNAL

WEEK 16 | DAY 3 | DATE

RUN 1

TIME/DISTANCE	WEATHER

COMMENTS

BAD RUN 1 2 3 4 5 6 7 8 9 10 GOOD RUN

NUTRITION

BEFORE	DURING	AFTER

RUN 2

TIME/DISTANCE	WEATHER

COMMENTS

BAD RUN 1 2 3 4 5 6 7 8 9 10 GOOD RUN

NUTRITION

BEFORE	DURING	AFTER

SPEEDWORK

1

TIME/DISTANCE	REPS	RECOVERY

2

TIME/DISTANCE	REPS	RECOVERY

MOOD	LOW	1	2	3	4	5	6	7	8	9	10	HIGH
ENERGY	LOW	1	2	3	4	5	6	7	8	9	10	HIGH
NUTRITION		1	2	3	4	5	6	7	8	9	10	
WATER 8oz		1	2	3	4	5	6	7	8	9	10	

SLEEP DIARY

WEEK 16 | DAY 4 | DATE

RUN

1

TIME/DISTANCE	WEATHER

COMMENTS

BAD RUN 1 2 3 4 5 6 7 8 9 10 GOOD RUN

NUTRITION

BEFORE	DURING	AFTER

RUN

2

TIME/DISTANCE	WEATHER

COMMENTS

BAD RUN 1 2 3 4 5 6 7 8 9 10 GOOD RUN

NUTRITION

BEFORE	DURING	AFTER

SPEEDWORK

1

TIME/DISTANCE	REPS	RECOVERY

2

TIME/DISTANCE	REPS	RECOVERY

MOOD	LOW	1	2	3	4	5	6	7	8	9	10	HIGH
ENERGY	LOW	1	2	3	4	5	6	7	8	9	10	HIGH
NUTRITION		1	2	3	4	5	6	7	8	9	10	
WATER 8oz		1	2	3	4	5	6	7	8	9	10	

SLEEP DIARY

RUN JOURNAL

WEEK 16 | DAY 5 | DATE

RUN 1

TIME/DISTANCE	WEATHER

COMMENTS

BAD RUN 1 2 3 4 5 6 7 8 9 10 GOOD RUN

NUTRITION

BEFORE	DURING	AFTER

RUN 2

TIME/DISTANCE	WEATHER

COMMENTS

BAD RUN 1 2 3 4 5 6 7 8 9 10 GOOD RUN

NUTRITION

BEFORE	DURING	AFTER

SPEEDWORK

1

TIME/DISTANCE	REPS	RECOVERY

2

TIME/DISTANCE	REPS	RECOVERY

MOOD	LOW	1	2	3	4	5	6	7	8	9	10	HIGH
ENERGY	LOW	1	2	3	4	5	6	7	8	9	10	HIGH
NUTRITION		1	2	3	4	5	6	7	8	9	10	
WATER 8oz		1	2	3	4	5	6	7	8	9	10	

SLEEP DIARY

WEEK 16 | DAY 6 | DATE

RUN
1

TIME/DISTANCE	WEATHER

COMMENTS

BAD RUN 1 2 3 4 5 6 7 8 9 10 GOOD RUN

NUTRITION

BEFORE	DURING	AFTER

RUN
2

TIME/DISTANCE	WEATHER

COMMENTS

BAD RUN 1 2 3 4 5 6 7 8 9 10 GOOD RUN

NUTRITION

BEFORE	DURING	AFTER

SPEEDWORK
1

TIME/DISTANCE	REPS	RECOVERY

2

TIME/DISTANCE	REPS	RECOVERY

MOOD	LOW	1	2	3	4	5	6	7	8	9	10	HIGH
ENERGY	LOW	1	2	3	4	5	6	7	8	9	10	HIGH
NUTRITION		1	2	3	4	5	6	7	8	9	10	
WATER 8oz		1	2	3	4	5	6	7	8	9	10	

SLEEP DIARY

RUN JOURNAL

WEEK 16 | DAY 7 | DATE

RUN 1

TIME/DISTANCE	WEATHER

COMMENTS

BAD RUN 1 2 3 4 5 6 7 8 9 10 GOOD RUN

NUTRITION

BEFORE	DURING	AFTER

RUN 2

TIME/DISTANCE	WEATHER

COMMENTS

BAD RUN 1 2 3 4 5 6 7 8 9 10 GOOD RUN

NUTRITION

BEFORE	DURING	AFTER

SPEEDWORK

1

TIME/DISTANCE	REPS	RECOVERY

2

TIME/DISTANCE	REPS	RECOVERY

MOOD	LOW	1	2	3	4	5	6	7	8	9	10	HIGH
ENERGY	LOW	1	2	3	4	5	6	7	8	9	10	HIGH
NUTRITION		1	2	3	4	5	6	7	8	9	10	
WATER 8oz		1	2	3	4	5	6	7	8	9	10	

SLEEP DIARY

WEEK 16 SUMMARY

DATE

GOALS MET

GOALS EXCEEDED

NEXT WEEK

RUNNING NOTES

SPEEDWORK NOTES

REFUELING NOTES

	Calories consumed	
MINUS	Calories Used	
EQUALS	Net Calories	
	BMR	
	net calories deficit	

VITAMINS	DOSAGE	QTY

MOOD

1 2 3 4 5 6 7 8 9 10

ENERGY LEVEL

1 2 3 4 5 6 7 8 9 10

Journal

MONTH 4 SUMMARY

GOALS MET | GOALS EXCEEDED | MAYBE NEXT WEEK

RUNNING NOTES

SPEEDWORK NOTES

MOOD & ENERGY

TOTAL RUNNING SESSIONS

TOTAL SPEEDWORK SESSIONS

GOALS FOR NEXT MONTH

RUN TRAINING GOALS	SPEED TRAINING GOALS

2-2 BREATHING RYTHYM

Most elite athletes uses this method to regulate their breathing. If you are new to running it is more important to achieve some kind of consistency. Good breathing is simply getting into a rhythm, as soon as you master this you will improve your running immediately.

Left foot – begin exhale
Right foot – continue exhale
Left foot – begin inhale
Right foot – continue inhale.

RUN JOURNAL

WEEK 17 | DAY 1 | DATE

RUN 1

TIME/DISTANCE	WEATHER

COMMENTS

BAD RUN 1 2 3 4 5 6 7 8 9 10 GOOD RUN

NUTRITION

BEFORE	DURING	AFTER

RUN 2

TIME/DISTANCE	WEATHER

COMMENTS

BAD RUN 1 2 3 4 5 6 7 8 9 10 GOOD RUN

NUTRITION

BEFORE	DURING	AFTER

SPEEDWORK

1

TIME/DISTANCE	REPS	RECOVERY

2

TIME/DISTANCE	REPS	RECOVERY

MOOD	LOW	1	2	3	4	5	6	7	8	9	10	HIGH
ENERGY	LOW	1	2	3	4	5	6	7	8	9	10	HIGH
NUTRITION		1	2	3	4	5	6	7	8	9	10	
WATER 8oz		1	2	3	4	5	6	7	8	9	10	

SLEEP DIARY

WEEK 17 | DAY 2 | DATE

RUN 1

TIME/DISTANCE	WEATHER

COMMENTS

BAD RUN	1	2	3	4	5	6	7	8	9	10	GOOD RUN

NUTRITION

BEFORE	DURING	AFTER

RUN 2

TIME/DISTANCE	WEATHER

COMMENTS

BAD RUN	1	2	3	4	5	6	7	8	9	10	GOOD RUN

NUTRITION

BEFORE	DURING	AFTER

SPEEDWORK

1

TIME/DISTANCE	REPS	RECOVERY

2

TIME/DISTANCE	REPS	RECOVERY

MOOD	LOW	1	2	3	4	5	6	7	8	9	10	HIGH
ENERGY	LOW	1	2	3	4	5	6	7	8	9	10	HIGH
NUTRITION		1	2	3	4	5	6	7	8	9	10	
WATER 8oz		1	2	3	4	5	6	7	8	9	10	

SLEEP DIARY

RUN JOURNAL

WEEK 17 | DAY 3 | DATE

RUN 1

TIME/DISTANCE	WEATHER

COMMENTS

BAD RUN 1 2 3 4 5 6 7 8 9 10 GOOD RUN

NUTRITION

BEFORE	DURING	AFTER

RUN 2

TIME/DISTANCE	WEATHER

COMMENTS

BAD RUN 1 2 3 4 5 6 7 8 9 10 GOOD RUN

NUTRITION

BEFORE	DURING	AFTER

SPEEDWORK

1

TIME/DISTANCE	REPS	RECOVERY

2

TIME/DISTANCE	REPS	RECOVERY

MOOD	LOW	1	2	3	4	5	6	7	8	9	10	HIGH
ENERGY	LOW	1	2	3	4	5	6	7	8	9	10	HIGH
NUTRITION		1	2	3	4	5	6	7	8	9	10	
WATER 8oz		1	2	3	4	5	6	7	8	9	10	

SLEEP DIARY

WEEK 17 | DAY 4 | DATE

RUN 1

TIME/DISTANCE	WEATHER

COMMENTS

BAD RUN	1	2	3	4	5	6	7	8	9	10	GOOD RUN

NUTRITION

BEFORE	DURING	AFTER

RUN 2

TIME/DISTANCE	WEATHER

COMMENTS

BAD RUN	1	2	3	4	5	6	7	8	9	10	GOOD RUN

NUTRITION

BEFORE	DURING	AFTER

SPEEDWORK

1

TIME/DISTANCE	REPS	RECOVERY

2

TIME/DISTANCE	REPS	RECOVERY

MOOD	LOW	1	2	3	4	5	6	7	8	9	10	HIGH
ENERGY	LOW	1	2	3	4	5	6	7	8	9	10	HIGH
NUTRITION		1	2	3	4	5	6	7	8	9	10	
WATER 8oz		1	2	3	4	5	6	7	8	9	10	

SLEEP DIARY

RUN JOURNAL

WEEK 17 | DAY 5 | DATE

RUN 1

TIME/DISTANCE	WEATHER

COMMENTS

BAD RUN 1 2 3 4 5 6 7 8 9 10 GOOD RUN

NUTRITION

BEFORE	DURING	AFTER

RUN 2

TIME/DISTANCE	WEATHER

COMMENTS

BAD RUN 1 2 3 4 5 6 7 8 9 10 GOOD RUN

NUTRITION

BEFORE	DURING	AFTER

SPEEDWORK

1

TIME/DISTANCE	REPS	RECOVERY

2

TIME/DISTANCE	REPS	RECOVERY

MOOD	LOW	1	2	3	4	5	6	7	8	9	10	HIGH
ENERGY	LOW	1	2	3	4	5	6	7	8	9	10	HIGH
NUTRITION		1	2	3	4	5	6	7	8	9	10	
WATER 8oz		1	2	3	4	5	6	7	8	9	10	

SLEEP DIARY

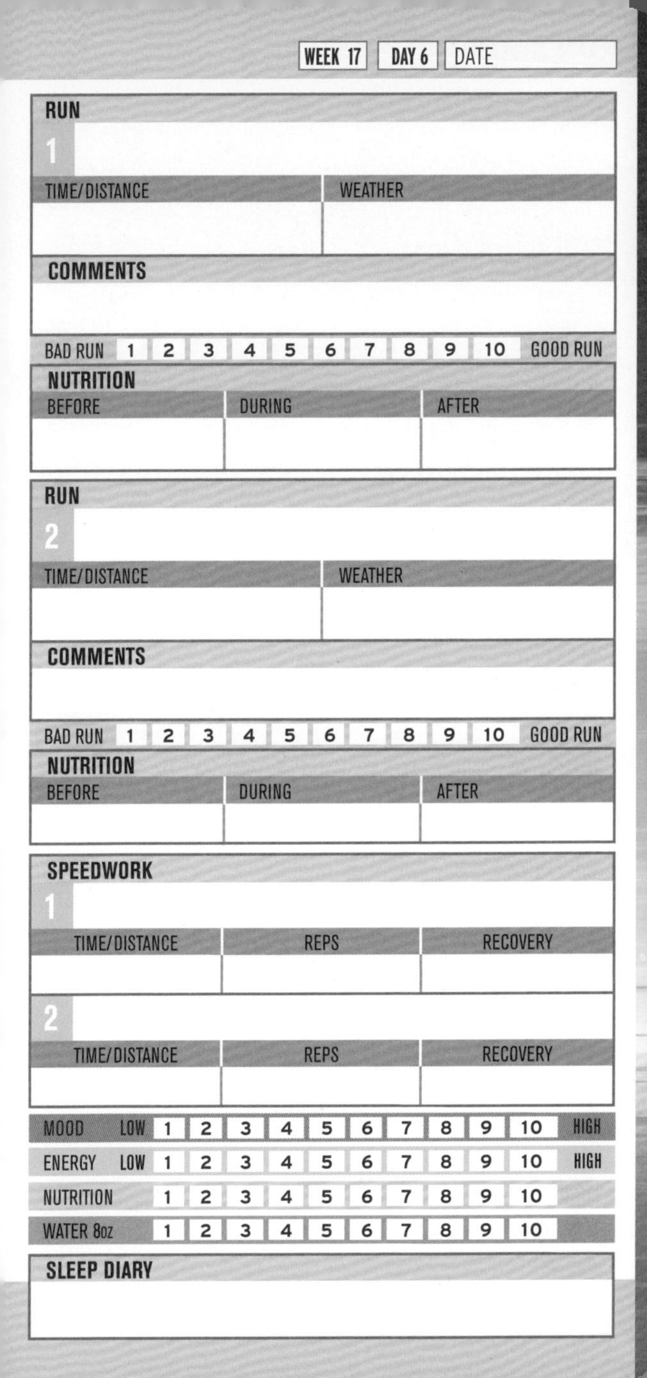

WEEK 17 | DAY 6 | DATE

RUN
1

TIME/DISTANCE	WEATHER

COMMENTS

BAD RUN 1 2 3 4 5 6 7 8 9 10 GOOD RUN

NUTRITION

BEFORE	DURING	AFTER

RUN
2

TIME/DISTANCE	WEATHER

COMMENTS

BAD RUN 1 2 3 4 5 6 7 8 9 10 GOOD RUN

NUTRITION

BEFORE	DURING	AFTER

SPEEDWORK
1

TIME/DISTANCE	REPS	RECOVERY

2

TIME/DISTANCE	REPS	RECOVERY

MOOD	LOW	1	2	3	4	5	6	7	8	9	10	HIGH
ENERGY	LOW	1	2	3	4	5	6	7	8	9	10	HIGH
NUTRITION		1	2	3	4	5	6	7	8	9	10	
WATER 8oz		1	2	3	4	5	6	7	8	9	10	

SLEEP DIARY

RUN JOURNAL

WEEK 17 | DAY 7 | DATE

RUN 1

TIME/DISTANCE	WEATHER

COMMENTS

BAD RUN 1 2 3 4 5 6 7 8 9 10 GOOD RUN

NUTRITION

BEFORE	DURING	AFTER

RUN 2

TIME/DISTANCE	WEATHER

COMMENTS

BAD RUN 1 2 3 4 5 6 7 8 9 10 GOOD RUN

NUTRITION

BEFORE	DURING	AFTER

SPEEDWORK

1

TIME/DISTANCE	REPS	RECOVERY

2

TIME/DISTANCE	REPS	RECOVERY

MOOD	LOW	1	2	3	4	5	6	7	8	9	10	HIGH
ENERGY	LOW	1	2	3	4	5	6	7	8	9	10	HIGH
NUTRITION		1	2	3	4	5	6	7	8	9	10	
WATER 8oz		1	2	3	4	5	6	7	8	9	10	

SLEEP DIARY

WEEK 17 SUMMARY

DATE

GOALS MET

GOALS EXCEEDED

NEXT WEEK

RUNNING NOTES

SPEEDWORK NOTES

REFUELING NOTES

	Calories consumed	
MINUS	Calories Used	
EQUALS	Net Calories	
	BMR	
	net calories deficit	

VITAMINS	DOSAGE	QTY

MOOD

1 2 3 4 5 6 7 8 9 10

ENERGY LEVEL

1 2 3 4 5 6 7 8 9 10

Journal

RUN JOURNAL

WEEK 18 | DAY 1 | DATE

RUN

1

TIME/DISTANCE | WEATHER

COMMENTS

BAD RUN 1 2 3 4 5 6 7 8 9 10 GOOD RUN

NUTRITION

BEFORE | DURING | AFTER

RUN

2

TIME/DISTANCE | WEATHER

COMMENTS

BAD RUN 1 2 3 4 5 6 7 8 9 10 GOOD RUN

NUTRITION

BEFORE | DURING | AFTER

SPEEDWORK

1

TIME/DISTANCE	REPS	RECOVERY

2

TIME/DISTANCE	REPS	RECOVERY

MOOD	LOW	1	2	3	4	5	6	7	8	9	10	HIGH
ENERGY	LOW	1	2	3	4	5	6	7	8	9	10	HIGH
NUTRITION		1	2	3	4	5	6	7	8	9	10	
WATER 8oz		1	2	3	4	5	6	7	8	9	10	

SLEEP DIARY

WEEK 18 | DAY 2 | DATE

RUN 1

TIME/DISTANCE	WEATHER

COMMENTS

BAD RUN 1 2 3 4 5 6 7 8 9 10 GOOD RUN

NUTRITION

BEFORE	DURING	AFTER

RUN 2

TIME/DISTANCE	WEATHER

COMMENTS

BAD RUN 1 2 3 4 5 6 7 8 9 10 GOOD RUN

NUTRITION

BEFORE	DURING	AFTER

SPEEDWORK

1

TIME/DISTANCE	REPS	RECOVERY

2

TIME/DISTANCE	REPS	RECOVERY

MOOD	LOW	1	2	3	4	5	6	7	8	9	10	HIGH
ENERGY	LOW	1	2	3	4	5	6	7	8	9	10	HIGH
NUTRITION		1	2	3	4	5	6	7	8	9	10	
WATER 8oz		1	2	3	4	5	6	7	8	9	10	

SLEEP DIARY

RUN JOURNAL

WEEK 18 | DAY 3 | DATE

RUN 1

TIME/DISTANCE	WEATHER

COMMENTS

BAD RUN 1 2 3 4 5 6 7 8 9 10 GOOD RUN

NUTRITION

BEFORE	DURING	AFTER

RUN 2

TIME/DISTANCE	WEATHER

COMMENTS

BAD RUN 1 2 3 4 5 6 7 8 9 10 GOOD RUN

NUTRITION

BEFORE	DURING	AFTER

SPEEDWORK

1

TIME/DISTANCE	REPS	RECOVERY

2

TIME/DISTANCE	REPS	RECOVERY

MOOD	LOW	1	2	3	4	5	6	7	8	9	10	HIGH
ENERGY	LOW	1	2	3	4	5	6	7	8	9	10	HIGH
NUTRITION		1	2	3	4	5	6	7	8	9	10	
WATER 8oz		1	2	3	4	5	6	7	8	9	10	

SLEEP DIARY

WEEK 18 | DAY 4 | DATE

RUN

1

TIME/DISTANCE	WEATHER

COMMENTS

BAD RUN	1	2	3	4	5	6	7	8	9	10	GOOD RUN

NUTRITION

BEFORE	DURING	AFTER

RUN

2

TIME/DISTANCE	WEATHER

COMMENTS

BAD RUN	1	2	3	4	5	6	7	8	9	10	GOOD RUN

NUTRITION

BEFORE	DURING	AFTER

SPEEDWORK

1

TIME/DISTANCE	REPS	RECOVERY

2

TIME/DISTANCE	REPS	RECOVERY

MOOD	LOW	1	2	3	4	5	6	7	8	9	10	HIGH
ENERGY	LOW	1	2	3	4	5	6	7	8	9	10	HIGH
NUTRITION		1	2	3	4	5	6	7	8	9	10	
WATER 8oz		1	2	3	4	5	6	7	8	9	10	

SLEEP DIARY

RUN JOURNAL

WEEK 18 | DAY 5 | DATE

RUN

1

TIME/DISTANCE	WEATHER

COMMENTS

BAD RUN 1 2 3 4 5 6 7 8 9 10 GOOD RUN

NUTRITION

BEFORE	DURING	AFTER

RUN

2

TIME/DISTANCE	WEATHER

COMMENTS

BAD RUN 1 2 3 4 5 6 7 8 9 10 GOOD RUN

NUTRITION

BEFORE	DURING	AFTER

SPEEDWORK

1

TIME/DISTANCE	REPS	RECOVERY

2

TIME/DISTANCE	REPS	RECOVERY

MOOD	LOW	1	2	3	4	5	6	7	8	9	10	HIGH
ENERGY	LOW	1	2	3	4	5	6	7	8	9	10	HIGH
NUTRITION		1	2	3	4	5	6	7	8	9	10	
WATER 8oz		1	2	3	4	5	6	7	8	9	10	

SLEEP DIARY

WEEK 18	DAY 6	DATE

RUN

1

TIME/DISTANCE	WEATHER

COMMENTS

BAD RUN 1 2 3 4 5 6 7 8 9 10 GOOD RUN

NUTRITION

BEFORE	DURING	AFTER

RUN

2

TIME/DISTANCE	WEATHER

COMMENTS

BAD RUN 1 2 3 4 5 6 7 8 9 10 GOOD RUN

NUTRITION

BEFORE	DURING	AFTER

SPEEDWORK

1

TIME/DISTANCE	REPS	RECOVERY

2

TIME/DISTANCE	REPS	RECOVERY

MOOD	LOW	1	2	3	4	5	6	7	8	9	10	HIGH
ENERGY	LOW	1	2	3	4	5	6	7	8	9	10	HIGH
NUTRITION		1	2	3	4	5	6	7	8	9	10	
WATER 8oz		1	2	3	4	5	6	7	8	9	10	

SLEEP DIARY

RUN JOURNAL

WEEK 18 | DAY 7 | DATE

RUN

1

TIME/DISTANCE	WEATHER

COMMENTS

BAD RUN 1 2 3 4 5 6 7 8 9 10 GOOD RUN

NUTRITION

BEFORE	DURING	AFTER

RUN

2

TIME/DISTANCE	WEATHER

COMMENTS

BAD RUN 1 2 3 4 5 6 7 8 9 10 GOOD RUN

NUTRITION

BEFORE	DURING	AFTER

SPEEDWORK

1

TIME/DISTANCE	REPS	RECOVERY

2

TIME/DISTANCE	REPS	RECOVERY

MOOD	LOW	1	2	3	4	5	6	7	8	9	10	HIGH
ENERGY	LOW	1	2	3	4	5	6	7	8	9	10	HIGH
NUTRITION		1	2	3	4	5	6	7	8	9	10	
WATER 8oz		1	2	3	4	5	6	7	8	9	10	

SLEEP DIARY

WEEK 18 SUMMARY

DATE

GOALS MET

GOALS EXCEEDED

NEXT WEEK

RUNNING NOTES

SPEEDWORK NOTES

REFUELING NOTES

	Calories consumed	
MINUS	Calories Used	
EQUALS	Net Calories	
	BMR	
	net calories deficit	

MOOD

1 2 3 4 5 6 7 8 9 10

ENERGY LEVEL

1 2 3 4 5 6 7 8 9 10

VITAMINS	DOSAGE	QTY

Journal

RUN JOURNAL

WEEK 19 | DAY 1 | DATE

RUN

1

TIME/DISTANCE	WEATHER

COMMENTS

BAD RUN 1 2 3 4 5 6 7 8 9 10 GOOD RUN

NUTRITION

BEFORE	DURING	AFTER

RUN

2

TIME/DISTANCE	WEATHER

COMMENTS

BAD RUN 1 2 3 4 5 6 7 8 9 10 GOOD RUN

NUTRITION

BEFORE	DURING	AFTER

SPEEDWORK

1

TIME/DISTANCE	REPS	RECOVERY

2

TIME/DISTANCE	REPS	RECOVERY

MOOD	LOW	1	2	3	4	5	6	7	8	9	10	HIGH
ENERGY	LOW	1	2	3	4	5	6	7	8	9	10	HIGH
NUTRITION		1	2	3	4	5	6	7	8	9	10	
WATER 8oz		1	2	3	4	5	6	7	8	9	10	

SLEEP DIARY

WEEK 19 | DAY 2 | DATE

RUN 1

TIME/DISTANCE	WEATHER

COMMENTS

BAD RUN 1 2 3 4 5 6 7 8 9 10 GOOD RUN

NUTRITION

BEFORE	DURING	AFTER

RUN 2

TIME/DISTANCE	WEATHER

COMMENTS

BAD RUN 1 2 3 4 5 6 7 8 9 10 GOOD RUN

NUTRITION

BEFORE	DURING	AFTER

SPEEDWORK

1

TIME/DISTANCE	REPS	RECOVERY

2

TIME/DISTANCE	REPS	RECOVERY

MOOD	LOW	1	2	3	4	5	6	7	8	9	10	HIGH
ENERGY	LOW	1	2	3	4	5	6	7	8	9	10	HIGH
NUTRITION		1	2	3	4	5	6	7	8	9	10	
WATER 8oz		1	2	3	4	5	6	7	8	9	10	

SLEEP DIARY

RUN JOURNAL

WEEK 19 | DAY 3 | DATE

RUN

1

TIME/DISTANCE	WEATHER

COMMENTS

BAD RUN	1	2	3	4	5	6	7	8	9	10	GOOD RUN

NUTRITION

BEFORE	DURING	AFTER

RUN

2

TIME/DISTANCE	WEATHER

COMMENTS

BAD RUN	1	2	3	4	5	6	7	8	9	10	GOOD RUN

NUTRITION

BEFORE	DURING	AFTER

SPEEDWORK

1

TIME/DISTANCE	REPS	RECOVERY

2

TIME/DISTANCE	REPS	RECOVERY

MOOD	LOW	1	2	3	4	5	6	7	8	9	10	HIGH
ENERGY	LOW	1	2	3	4	5	6	7	8	9	10	HIGH
NUTRITION		1	2	3	4	5	6	7	8	9	10	
WATER 8oz		1	2	3	4	5	6	7	8	9	10	

SLEEP DIARY

RUN 1

TIME/DISTANCE	WEATHER

COMMENTS

BAD RUN 1 2 3 4 5 6 7 8 9 10 GOOD RUN

NUTRITION

BEFORE	DURING	AFTER

RUN 2

TIME/DISTANCE	WEATHER

COMMENTS

BAD RUN 1 2 3 4 5 6 7 8 9 10 GOOD RUN

NUTRITION

BEFORE	DURING	AFTER

SPEEDWORK

1

TIME/DISTANCE	REPS	RECOVERY

2

TIME/DISTANCE	REPS	RECOVERY

MOOD	LOW	1	2	3	4	5	6	7	8	9	10	HIGH
ENERGY	LOW	1	2	3	4	5	6	7	8	9	10	HIGH
NUTRITION		1	2	3	4	5	6	7	8	9	10	
WATER 8oz		1	2	3	4	5	6	7	8	9	10	

SLEEP DIARY

RUN JOURNAL

WEEK 19 | DAY 5 | DATE

RUN 1

TIME/DISTANCE	WEATHER

COMMENTS

BAD RUN 1 2 3 4 5 6 7 8 9 10 GOOD RUN

NUTRITION

BEFORE	DURING	AFTER

RUN 2

TIME/DISTANCE	WEATHER

COMMENTS

BAD RUN 1 2 3 4 5 6 7 8 9 10 GOOD RUN

NUTRITION

BEFORE	DURING	AFTER

SPEEDWORK

1

TIME/DISTANCE	REPS	RECOVERY

2

TIME/DISTANCE	REPS	RECOVERY

MOOD	LOW	1	2	3	4	5	6	7	8	9	10	HIGH
ENERGY	LOW	1	2	3	4	5	6	7	8	9	10	HIGH
NUTRITION		1	2	3	4	5	6	7	8	9	10	
WATER 8oz		1	2	3	4	5	6	7	8	9	10	

SLEEP DIARY

WEEK 19 | DAY 6 | DATE

RUN 1

TIME/DISTANCE	WEATHER

COMMENTS

BAD RUN 1 2 3 4 5 6 7 8 9 10 GOOD RUN

NUTRITION

BEFORE	DURING	AFTER

RUN 2

TIME/DISTANCE	WEATHER

COMMENTS

BAD RUN 1 2 3 4 5 6 7 8 9 10 GOOD RUN

NUTRITION

BEFORE	DURING	AFTER

SPEEDWORK

1

TIME/DISTANCE	REPS	RECOVERY

2

TIME/DISTANCE	REPS	RECOVERY

MOOD	LOW	1	2	3	4	5	6	7	8	9	10	HIGH
ENERGY	LOW	1	2	3	4	5	6	7	8	9	10	HIGH
NUTRITION		1	2	3	4	5	6	7	8	9	10	
WATER 8oz		1	2	3	4	5	6	7	8	9	10	

SLEEP DIARY

RUN JOURNAL

WEEK 19 | DAY 7 | DATE

RUN 1

TIME/DISTANCE	WEATHER

COMMENTS

BAD RUN 1 2 3 4 5 6 7 8 9 10 GOOD RUN

NUTRITION

BEFORE	DURING	AFTER

RUN 2

TIME/DISTANCE	WEATHER

COMMENTS

BAD RUN 1 2 3 4 5 6 7 8 9 10 GOOD RUN

NUTRITION

BEFORE	DURING	AFTER

SPEEDWORK

1

TIME/DISTANCE	REPS	RECOVERY

2

TIME/DISTANCE	REPS	RECOVERY

MOOD	LOW	1	2	3	4	5	6	7	8	9	10	HIGH
ENERGY	LOW	1	2	3	4	5	6	7	8	9	10	HIGH
NUTRITION		1	2	3	4	5	6	7	8	9	10	
WATER 8oz		1	2	3	4	5	6	7	8	9	10	

SLEEP DIARY

WEEK 19 SUMMARY

DATE

GOALS MET

GOALS EXCEEDED

NEXT WEEK

RUNNING NOTES

SPEEDWORK NOTES

REFUELING NOTES

	Calories consumed	
MINUS	Calories Used	
EQUALS	Net Calories	
	BMR	
	net calories deficit	

VITAMINS	DOSAGE	QTY

MOOD

1 2 3 4 5 6 7 8 9 10

ENERGY LEVEL

1 2 3 4 5 6 7 8 9 10

Journal

RUN JOURNAL

WEEK 20 | DAY 1 | DATE

RUN 1

TIME/DISTANCE	WEATHER

COMMENTS

BAD RUN 1 2 3 4 5 6 7 8 9 10 GOOD RUN

NUTRITION

BEFORE	DURING	AFTER

RUN 2

TIME/DISTANCE	WEATHER

COMMENTS

BAD RUN 1 2 3 4 5 6 7 8 9 10 GOOD RUN

NUTRITION

BEFORE	DURING	AFTER

SPEEDWORK

1

TIME/DISTANCE	REPS	RECOVERY

2

TIME/DISTANCE	REPS	RECOVERY

MOOD	LOW	1	2	3	4	5	6	7	8	9	10	HIGH
ENERGY	LOW	1	2	3	4	5	6	7	8	9	10	HIGH
NUTRITION		1	2	3	4	5	6	7	8	9	10	
WATER 8oz		1	2	3	4	5	6	7	8	9	10	

SLEEP DIARY

WEEK 20 | DAY 2 | DATE

RUN

1

TIME/DISTANCE	WEATHER

COMMENTS

BAD RUN 1 2 3 4 5 6 7 8 9 10 GOOD RUN

NUTRITION

BEFORE	DURING	AFTER

RUN

2

TIME/DISTANCE	WEATHER

COMMENTS

BAD RUN 1 2 3 4 5 6 7 8 9 10 GOOD RUN

NUTRITION

BEFORE	DURING	AFTER

SPEEDWORK

1

TIME/DISTANCE	REPS	RECOVERY

2

TIME/DISTANCE	REPS	RECOVERY

MOOD	LOW	1	2	3	4	5	6	7	8	9	10	HIGH
ENERGY	LOW	1	2	3	4	5	6	7	8	9	10	HIGH
NUTRITION		1	2	3	4	5	6	7	8	9	10	
WATER 8oz		1	2	3	4	5	6	7	8	9	10	

SLEEP DIARY

RUN JOURNAL

WEEK 20 | DAY 3 | DATE

RUN 1

TIME/DISTANCE	WEATHER

COMMENTS

BAD RUN 1 2 3 4 5 6 7 8 9 10 GOOD RUN

NUTRITION

BEFORE	DURING	AFTER

RUN 2

TIME/DISTANCE	WEATHER

COMMENTS

BAD RUN 1 2 3 4 5 6 7 8 9 10 GOOD RUN

NUTRITION

BEFORE	DURING	AFTER

SPEEDWORK

1

TIME/DISTANCE	REPS	RECOVERY

2

TIME/DISTANCE	REPS	RECOVERY

MOOD	LOW	1	2	3	4	5	6	7	8	9	10	HIGH
ENERGY	LOW	1	2	3	4	5	6	7	8	9	10	HIGH
NUTRITION		1	2	3	4	5	6	7	8	9	10	
WATER 8oz		1	2	3	4	5	6	7	8	9	10	

SLEEP DIARY

WEEK 20 | DAY 4 | DATE

RUN

1

TIME/DISTANCE	WEATHER

COMMENTS

BAD RUN 1 2 3 4 5 6 7 8 9 10 GOOD RUN

NUTRITION

BEFORE	DURING	AFTER

RUN

2

TIME/DISTANCE	WEATHER

COMMENTS

BAD RUN 1 2 3 4 5 6 7 8 9 10 GOOD RUN

NUTRITION

BEFORE	DURING	AFTER

SPEEDWORK

1

TIME/DISTANCE	REPS	RECOVERY

2

TIME/DISTANCE	REPS	RECOVERY

MOOD	LOW	1	2	3	4	5	6	7	8	9	10	HIGH
ENERGY	LOW	1	2	3	4	5	6	7	8	9	10	HIGH
NUTRITION		1	2	3	4	5	6	7	8	9	10	
WATER 8oz		1	2	3	4	5	6	7	8	9	10	

SLEEP DIARY

RUN JOURNAL

WEEK 20 | DAY 5 | DATE

RUN 1

TIME/DISTANCE	WEATHER

COMMENTS

BAD RUN 1 2 3 4 5 6 7 8 9 10 GOOD RUN

NUTRITION

BEFORE	DURING	AFTER

RUN 2

TIME/DISTANCE	WEATHER

COMMENTS

BAD RUN 1 2 3 4 5 6 7 8 9 10 GOOD RUN

NUTRITION

BEFORE	DURING	AFTER

SPEEDWORK

1

TIME/DISTANCE	REPS	RECOVERY

2

TIME/DISTANCE	REPS	RECOVERY

MOOD	LOW	1	2	3	4	5	6	7	8	9	10	HIGH
ENERGY	LOW	1	2	3	4	5	6	7	8	9	10	HIGH
NUTRITION		1	2	3	4	5	6	7	8	9	10	
WATER 8oz		1	2	3	4	5	6	7	8	9	10	

SLEEP DIARY

WEEK 20 | DAY 6 | DATE

RUN 1

TIME/DISTANCE	WEATHER

COMMENTS

BAD RUN 1 2 3 4 5 6 7 8 9 10 GOOD RUN

NUTRITION

BEFORE	DURING	AFTER

RUN 2

TIME/DISTANCE	WEATHER

COMMENTS

BAD RUN 1 2 3 4 5 6 7 8 9 10 GOOD RUN

NUTRITION

BEFORE	DURING	AFTER

SPEEDWORK

1

TIME/DISTANCE	REPS	RECOVERY

2

TIME/DISTANCE	REPS	RECOVERY

MOOD	LOW	1	2	3	4	5	6	7	8	9	10	HIGH
ENERGY	LOW	1	2	3	4	5	6	7	8	9	10	HIGH
NUTRITION		1	2	3	4	5	6	7	8	9	10	
WATER 8oz		1	2	3	4	5	6	7	8	9	10	

SLEEP DIARY

RUN JOURNAL

WEEK 20 | DAY 7 | DATE

RUN 1

TIME/DISTANCE	WEATHER

COMMENTS

BAD RUN 1 2 3 4 5 6 7 8 9 10 GOOD RUN

NUTRITION

BEFORE	DURING	AFTER

RUN 2

TIME/DISTANCE	WEATHER

COMMENTS

BAD RUN 1 2 3 4 5 6 7 8 9 10 GOOD RUN

NUTRITION

BEFORE	DURING	AFTER

SPEEDWORK

1

TIME/DISTANCE	REPS	RECOVERY

2

TIME/DISTANCE	REPS	RECOVERY

MOOD	LOW	1	2	3	4	5	6	7	8	9	10	HIGH
ENERGY	LOW	1	2	3	4	5	6	7	8	9	10	HIGH
NUTRITION		1	2	3	4	5	6	7	8	9	10	
WATER 8oz		1	2	3	4	5	6	7	8	9	10	

SLEEP DIARY

WEEK 20 SUMMARY

DATE

GOALS MET

GOALS EXCEEDED

NEXT WEEK

RUNNING NOTES

SPEEDWORK NOTES

REFUELING NOTES

	Calories consumed	
MINUS	Calories Used	
EQUALS	Net Calories	
	BMR	
	net calories deficit	

MOOD

1 2 3 4 5 6 7 8 9 10

ENERGY LEVEL

1 2 3 4 5 6 7 8 9 10

VITAMINS	DOSAGE	QTY

Journal

RUN JOURNAL

MONTH 5 | DATE

MONTH 5 SUMMARY

GOALS MET | GOALS EXCEEDED | MAYBE NEXT WEEK

RUNNING NOTES

SPEEDWORK NOTES

MOOD & ENERGY

TOTAL RUNNING SESSIONS

TOTAL SPEEDWORK SESSIONS

GOALS FOR NEXT MONTH

RUN TRAINING GOALS	SPEED TRAINING GOALS

HOW TO RUN FASTER

Preparation is so important if you want to learn how to run faster. Make sure that you fuel your body correctly , try having 500ml of water and a banana 20 minutes before a run and see if this brings your time down. Make sure you warm up, if you don't your body will use the first few minutes to warm up and in the first five minutes you will lose time on the run. So get warm before you start. Try press ups to warm your chest and arms, hip rotations to warm your lower back and core, and one minute of jumping jacks to get your heart rate going and then set off.

RUN JOURNAL

WEEK 21 | DAY 1 | DATE

RUN

1

TIME/DISTANCE	WEATHER

COMMENTS

BAD RUN 1 2 3 4 5 6 7 8 9 10 GOOD RUN

NUTRITION

BEFORE	DURING	AFTER

RUN

2

TIME/DISTANCE	WEATHER

COMMENTS

BAD RUN 1 2 3 4 5 6 7 8 9 10 GOOD RUN

NUTRITION

BEFORE	DURING	AFTER

SPEEDWORK

1

TIME/DISTANCE	REPS	RECOVERY

2

TIME/DISTANCE	REPS	RECOVERY

MOOD	LOW	1	2	3	4	5	6	7	8	9	10	HIGH
ENERGY	LOW	1	2	3	4	5	6	7	8	9	10	HIGH
NUTRITION		1	2	3	4	5	6	7	8	9	10	
WATER 8oz		1	2	3	4	5	6	7	8	9	10	

SLEEP DIARY

WEEK 21 | DAY 2 | DATE

RUN 1

TIME/DISTANCE	WEATHER

COMMENTS

BAD RUN	1	2	3	4	5	6	7	8	9	10	GOOD RUN

NUTRITION

BEFORE	DURING	AFTER

RUN 2

TIME/DISTANCE	WEATHER

COMMENTS

BAD RUN	1	2	3	4	5	6	7	8	9	10	GOOD RUN

NUTRITION

BEFORE	DURING	AFTER

SPEEDWORK

1

TIME/DISTANCE	REPS	RECOVERY

2

TIME/DISTANCE	REPS	RECOVERY

MOOD	LOW	1	2	3	4	5	6	7	8	9	10	HIGH
ENERGY	LOW	1	2	3	4	5	6	7	8	9	10	HIGH
NUTRITION		1	2	3	4	5	6	7	8	9	10	
WATER 8oz		1	2	3	4	5	6	7	8	9	10	

SLEEP DIARY

RUN JOURNAL

WEEK 21 | DAY 3 | DATE

RUN 1

TIME/DISTANCE	WEATHER

COMMENTS

BAD RUN 1 2 3 4 5 6 7 8 9 10 GOOD RUN

NUTRITION

BEFORE	DURING	AFTER

RUN 2

TIME/DISTANCE	WEATHER

COMMENTS

BAD RUN 1 2 3 4 5 6 7 8 9 10 GOOD RUN

NUTRITION

BEFORE	DURING	AFTER

SPEEDWORK

1

TIME/DISTANCE	REPS	RECOVERY

2

TIME/DISTANCE	REPS	RECOVERY

MOOD	LOW	1	2	3	4	5	6	7	8	9	10	HIGH
ENERGY	LOW	1	2	3	4	5	6	7	8	9	10	HIGH
NUTRITION		1	2	3	4	5	6	7	8	9	10	
WATER 8oz		1	2	3	4	5	6	7	8	9	10	

SLEEP DIARY

WEEK 21 | DAY 4 | DATE

RUN

1

TIME/DISTANCE	WEATHER

COMMENTS

BAD RUN 1 2 3 4 5 6 7 8 9 10 GOOD RUN

NUTRITION

BEFORE	DURING	AFTER

RUN

2

TIME/DISTANCE	WEATHER

COMMENTS

BAD RUN 1 2 3 4 5 6 7 8 9 10 GOOD RUN

NUTRITION

BEFORE	DURING	AFTER

SPEEDWORK

1

TIME/DISTANCE	REPS	RECOVERY

2

TIME/DISTANCE	REPS	RECOVERY

MOOD	LOW	1	2	3	4	5	6	7	8	9	10	HIGH
ENERGY	LOW	1	2	3	4	5	6	7	8	9	10	HIGH
NUTRITION		1	2	3	4	5	6	7	8	9	10	
WATER 8oz		1	2	3	4	5	6	7	8	9	10	

SLEEP DIARY

RUN JOURNAL

WEEK 21 | DAY 5 | DATE

RUN 1

TIME/DISTANCE	WEATHER

COMMENTS

BAD RUN 1 2 3 4 5 6 7 8 9 10 GOOD RUN

NUTRITION

BEFORE	DURING	AFTER

RUN 2

TIME/DISTANCE	WEATHER

COMMENTS

BAD RUN 1 2 3 4 5 6 7 8 9 10 GOOD RUN

NUTRITION

BEFORE	DURING	AFTER

SPEEDWORK

1

TIME/DISTANCE	REPS	RECOVERY

2

TIME/DISTANCE	REPS	RECOVERY

MOOD	LOW	1	2	3	4	5	6	7	8	9	10	HIGH
ENERGY	LOW	1	2	3	4	5	6	7	8	9	10	HIGH
NUTRITION		1	2	3	4	5	6	7	8	9	10	
WATER 8oz		1	2	3	4	5	6	7	8	9	10	

SLEEP DIARY

WEEK 21 | DAY 6 | DATE

RUN 1

TIME/DISTANCE | WEATHER

COMMENTS

BAD RUN 1 2 3 4 5 6 7 8 9 10 GOOD RUN

NUTRITION

BEFORE	DURING	AFTER

RUN 2

TIME/DISTANCE | WEATHER

COMMENTS

BAD RUN 1 2 3 4 5 6 7 8 9 10 GOOD RUN

NUTRITION

BEFORE	DURING	AFTER

SPEEDWORK

1

TIME/DISTANCE	REPS	RECOVERY

2

TIME/DISTANCE	REPS	RECOVERY

MOOD	LOW	1	2	3	4	5	6	7	8	9	10	HIGH
ENERGY	LOW	1	2	3	4	5	6	7	8	9	10	HIGH
NUTRITION		1	2	3	4	5	6	7	8	9	10	
WATER 8oz		1	2	3	4	5	6	7	8	9	10	

SLEEP DIARY

RUN JOURNAL

WEEK 21 | DAY 7 | DATE

RUN

1

TIME/DISTANCE	WEATHER

COMMENTS

BAD RUN 1 2 3 4 5 6 7 8 9 10 GOOD RUN

NUTRITION

BEFORE	DURING	AFTER

RUN

2

TIME/DISTANCE	WEATHER

COMMENTS

BAD RUN 1 2 3 4 5 6 7 8 9 10 GOOD RUN

NUTRITION

BEFORE	DURING	AFTER

SPEEDWORK

1

TIME/DISTANCE	REPS	RECOVERY

2

TIME/DISTANCE	REPS	RECOVERY

MOOD	LOW	1	2	3	4	5	6	7	8	9	10	HIGH
ENERGY	LOW	1	2	3	4	5	6	7	8	9	10	HIGH
NUTRITION		1	2	3	4	5	6	7	8	9	10	
WATER 8oz		1	2	3	4	5	6	7	8	9	10	

SLEEP DIARY

WEEK 21 SUMMARY

DATE

GOALS MET

GOALS EXCEEDED

NEXT WEEK

RUNNING NOTES

SPEEDWORK NOTES

REFUELING NOTES

	Calories consumed	
MINUS	Calories Used	
EQUALS	Net Calories	
	BMR	
	net calories deficit	

VITAMINS	DOSAGE	QTY

MOOD

1 2 3 4 5 6 7 8 9 10

ENERGY LEVEL

1 2 3 4 5 6 7 8 9 10

Journal

RUN JOURNAL

WEEK 22 | DAY 1 | DATE

RUN 1

TIME/DISTANCE	WEATHER

COMMENTS

BAD RUN 1 2 3 4 5 6 7 8 9 10 GOOD RUN

NUTRITION

BEFORE	DURING	AFTER

RUN 2

TIME/DISTANCE	WEATHER

COMMENTS

BAD RUN 1 2 3 4 5 6 7 8 9 10 GOOD RUN

NUTRITION

BEFORE	DURING	AFTER

SPEEDWORK

1

TIME/DISTANCE	REPS	RECOVERY

2

TIME/DISTANCE	REPS	RECOVERY

MOOD	LOW	1	2	3	4	5	6	7	8	9	10	HIGH
ENERGY	LOW	1	2	3	4	5	6	7	8	9	10	HIGH
NUTRITION		1	2	3	4	5	6	7	8	9	10	
WATER 8oz		1	2	3	4	5	6	7	8	9	10	

SLEEP DIARY

WEEK 22 | DAY 2 | DATE

RUN

1

TIME/DISTANCE	WEATHER

COMMENTS

BAD RUN 1 2 3 4 5 6 7 8 9 10 GOOD RUN

NUTRITION

BEFORE	DURING	AFTER

RUN

2

TIME/DISTANCE	WEATHER

COMMENTS

BAD RUN 1 2 3 4 5 6 7 8 9 10 GOOD RUN

NUTRITION

BEFORE	DURING	AFTER

SPEEDWORK

1

TIME/DISTANCE	REPS	RECOVERY

2

TIME/DISTANCE	REPS	RECOVERY

MOOD	LOW	1	2	3	4	5	6	7	8	9	10	HIGH
ENERGY	LOW	1	2	3	4	5	6	7	8	9	10	HIGH
NUTRITION		1	2	3	4	5	6	7	8	9	10	
WATER 8oz		1	2	3	4	5	6	7	8	9	10	

SLEEP DIARY

RUN JOURNAL

WEEK 22 | DAY 3 | DATE

RUN

1

TIME/DISTANCE	WEATHER

COMMENTS

BAD RUN 1 2 3 4 5 6 7 8 9 10 GOOD RUN

NUTRITION

BEFORE	DURING	AFTER

RUN

2

TIME/DISTANCE	WEATHER

COMMENTS

BAD RUN 1 2 3 4 5 6 7 8 9 10 GOOD RUN

NUTRITION

BEFORE	DURING	AFTER

SPEEDWORK

1

TIME/DISTANCE	REPS	RECOVERY

2

TIME/DISTANCE	REPS	RECOVERY

MOOD	LOW	1	2	3	4	5	6	7	8	9	10	HIGH
ENERGY	LOW	1	2	3	4	5	6	7	8	9	10	HIGH
NUTRITION		1	2	3	4	5	6	7	8	9	10	
WATER 8oz		1	2	3	4	5	6	7	8	9	10	

SLEEP DIARY

RUN

1

TIME/DISTANCE	WEATHER

COMMENTS

BAD RUN 1 2 3 4 5 6 7 8 9 10 GOOD RUN

NUTRITION

BEFORE	DURING	AFTER

RUN

2

TIME/DISTANCE	WEATHER

COMMENTS

BAD RUN 1 2 3 4 5 6 7 8 9 10 GOOD RUN

NUTRITION

BEFORE	DURING	AFTER

SPEEDWORK

1

TIME/DISTANCE	REPS	RECOVERY

2

TIME/DISTANCE	REPS	RECOVERY

MOOD	LOW	1	2	3	4	5	6	7	8	9	10	HIGH
ENERGY	LOW	1	2	3	4	5	6	7	8	9	10	HIGH
NUTRITION		1	2	3	4	5	6	7	8	9	10	
WATER 8oz		1	2	3	4	5	6	7	8	9	10	

SLEEP DIARY

RUN JOURNAL

WEEK 22 | DAY 5 | DATE

RUN 1

TIME/DISTANCE	WEATHER

COMMENTS

BAD RUN 1 2 3 4 5 6 7 8 9 10 GOOD RUN

NUTRITION

BEFORE	DURING	AFTER

RUN 2

TIME/DISTANCE	WEATHER

COMMENTS

BAD RUN 1 2 3 4 5 6 7 8 9 10 GOOD RUN

NUTRITION

BEFORE	DURING	AFTER

SPEEDWORK

1

TIME/DISTANCE	REPS	RECOVERY

2

TIME/DISTANCE	REPS	RECOVERY

MOOD	LOW	1	2	3	4	5	6	7	8	9	10	HIGH
ENERGY	LOW	1	2	3	4	5	6	7	8	9	10	HIGH
NUTRITION		1	2	3	4	5	6	7	8	9	10	
WATER 8oz		1	2	3	4	5	6	7	8	9	10	

SLEEP DIARY

WEEK 22 | DAY 6 | DATE

RUN 1

TIME/DISTANCE	WEATHER

COMMENTS

BAD RUN 1 2 3 4 5 6 7 8 9 10 GOOD RUN

NUTRITION

BEFORE	DURING	AFTER

RUN 2

TIME/DISTANCE	WEATHER

COMMENTS

BAD RUN 1 2 3 4 5 6 7 8 9 10 GOOD RUN

NUTRITION

BEFORE	DURING	AFTER

SPEEDWORK

1

TIME/DISTANCE	REPS	RECOVERY

2

TIME/DISTANCE	REPS	RECOVERY

MOOD	LOW	1	2	3	4	5	6	7	8	9	10	HIGH
ENERGY	LOW	1	2	3	4	5	6	7	8	9	10	HIGH
NUTRITION		1	2	3	4	5	6	7	8	9	10	
WATER 8oz		1	2	3	4	5	6	7	8	9	10	

SLEEP DIARY

RUN JOURNAL

WEEK 22 | DAY 7 | DATE

RUN 1

TIME/DISTANCE	WEATHER

COMMENTS

BAD RUN 1 2 3 4 5 6 7 8 9 10 GOOD RUN

NUTRITION

BEFORE	DURING	AFTER

RUN 2

TIME/DISTANCE	WEATHER

COMMENTS

BAD RUN 1 2 3 4 5 6 7 8 9 10 GOOD RUN

NUTRITION

BEFORE	DURING	AFTER

SPEEDWORK

1

TIME/DISTANCE	REPS	RECOVERY

2

TIME/DISTANCE	REPS	RECOVERY

MOOD	LOW	1	2	3	4	5	6	7	8	9	10	HIGH
ENERGY	LOW	1	2	3	4	5	6	7	8	9	10	HIGH
NUTRITION		1	2	3	4	5	6	7	8	9	10	
WATER 8oz		1	2	3	4	5	6	7	8	9	10	

SLEEP DIARY

WEEK 22 SUMMARY

DATE

GOALS MET

GOALS EXCEEDED

NEXT WEEK

RUNNING NOTES

SPEEDWORK NOTES

REFUELING NOTES

Calories consumed	
MINUS Calories Used	
EQUALS Net Calories	
BMR	
net calories deficit	

MOOD

1 2 3 4 5 6 7 8 9 10

ENERGY LEVEL

1 2 3 4 5 6 7 8 9 10

VITAMINS	DOSAGE	QTY

Journal

RUN JOURNAL

WEEK 23 | DAY 1 | DATE

RUN 1

TIME/DISTANCE	WEATHER

COMMENTS

BAD RUN 1 2 3 4 5 6 7 8 9 10 GOOD RUN

NUTRITION

BEFORE	DURING	AFTER

RUN 2

TIME/DISTANCE	WEATHER

COMMENTS

BAD RUN 1 2 3 4 5 6 7 8 9 10 GOOD RUN

NUTRITION

BEFORE	DURING	AFTER

SPEEDWORK

1

TIME/DISTANCE	REPS	RECOVERY

2

TIME/DISTANCE	REPS	RECOVERY

MOOD	LOW	1	2	3	4	5	6	7	8	9	10	HIGH
ENERGY	LOW	1	2	3	4	5	6	7	8	9	10	HIGH
NUTRITION		1	2	3	4	5	6	7	8	9	10	
WATER 8oz		1	2	3	4	5	6	7	8	9	10	

SLEEP DIARY

WEEK 23 | DAY 2 | DATE

RUN 1

TIME/DISTANCE	WEATHER

COMMENTS

BAD RUN 1 2 3 4 5 6 7 8 9 10 GOOD RUN

NUTRITION

BEFORE	DURING	AFTER

RUN 2

TIME/DISTANCE	WEATHER

COMMENTS

BAD RUN 1 2 3 4 5 6 7 8 9 10 GOOD RUN

NUTRITION

BEFORE	DURING	AFTER

SPEEDWORK

1

TIME/DISTANCE	REPS	RECOVERY

2

TIME/DISTANCE	REPS	RECOVERY

MOOD	LOW	1	2	3	4	5	6	7	8	9	10	HIGH
ENERGY	LOW	1	2	3	4	5	6	7	8	9	10	HIGH
NUTRITION		1	2	3	4	5	6	7	8	9	10	
WATER 8oz		1	2	3	4	5	6	7	8	9	10	

SLEEP DIARY

RUN JOURNAL

WEEK 23 | DAY 3 | DATE

RUN

1

TIME/DISTANCE	WEATHER

COMMENTS

BAD RUN	1	2	3	4	5	6	7	8	9	10	GOOD RUN

NUTRITION

BEFORE	DURING	AFTER

RUN

2

TIME/DISTANCE	WEATHER

COMMENTS

BAD RUN	1	2	3	4	5	6	7	8	9	10	GOOD RUN

NUTRITION

BEFORE	DURING	AFTER

SPEEDWORK

1

TIME/DISTANCE	REPS	RECOVERY

2

TIME/DISTANCE	REPS	RECOVERY

MOOD	LOW	1	2	3	4	5	6	7	8	9	10	HIGH
ENERGY	LOW	1	2	3	4	5	6	7	8	9	10	HIGH
NUTRITION		1	2	3	4	5	6	7	8	9	10	
WATER 8oz		1	2	3	4	5	6	7	8	9	10	

SLEEP DIARY

RUN 1

TIME/DISTANCE	WEATHER

COMMENTS

BAD RUN 1 2 3 4 5 6 7 8 9 10 GOOD RUN

NUTRITION

BEFORE	DURING	AFTER

RUN 2

TIME/DISTANCE	WEATHER

COMMENTS

BAD RUN 1 2 3 4 5 6 7 8 9 10 GOOD RUN

NUTRITION

BEFORE	DURING	AFTER

SPEEDWORK

1

TIME/DISTANCE	REPS	RECOVERY

2

TIME/DISTANCE	REPS	RECOVERY

MOOD	LOW	1	2	3	4	5	6	7	8	9	10	HIGH
ENERGY	LOW	1	2	3	4	5	6	7	8	9	10	HIGH
NUTRITION		1	2	3	4	5	6	7	8	9	10	
WATER 8oz		1	2	3	4	5	6	7	8	9	10	

SLEEP DIARY

RUN JOURNAL

WEEK 23 | DAY 5 | DATE

RUN

1

TIME/DISTANCE	WEATHER

COMMENTS

BAD RUN 1 2 3 4 5 6 7 8 9 10 GOOD RUN

NUTRITION

BEFORE	DURING	AFTER

RUN

2

TIME/DISTANCE	WEATHER

COMMENTS

BAD RUN 1 2 3 4 5 6 7 8 9 10 GOOD RUN

NUTRITION

BEFORE	DURING	AFTER

SPEEDWORK

1

TIME/DISTANCE	REPS	RECOVERY

2

TIME/DISTANCE	REPS	RECOVERY

MOOD	LOW	1	2	3	4	5	6	7	8	9	10	HIGH
ENERGY	LOW	1	2	3	4	5	6	7	8	9	10	HIGH
NUTRITION		1	2	3	4	5	6	7	8	9	10	
WATER 8oz		1	2	3	4	5	6	7	8	9	10	

SLEEP DIARY

WEEK 23 | DAY 6 | DATE

RUN 1

TIME/DISTANCE	WEATHER

COMMENTS

BAD RUN 1 2 3 4 5 6 7 8 9 10 GOOD RUN

NUTRITION

BEFORE	DURING	AFTER

RUN 2

TIME/DISTANCE	WEATHER

COMMENTS

BAD RUN 1 2 3 4 5 6 7 8 9 10 GOOD RUN

NUTRITION

BEFORE	DURING	AFTER

SPEEDWORK

1

TIME/DISTANCE	REPS	RECOVERY

2

TIME/DISTANCE	REPS	RECOVERY

MOOD	LOW	1	2	3	4	5	6	7	8	9	10	HIGH
ENERGY	LOW	1	2	3	4	5	6	7	8	9	10	HIGH
NUTRITION		1	2	3	4	5	6	7	8	9	10	
WATER 8oz		1	2	3	4	5	6	7	8	9	10	

SLEEP DIARY

RUN JOURNAL

WEEK 23 | DAY 7 | DATE

RUN 1

TIME/DISTANCE	WEATHER

COMMENTS

BAD RUN 1 2 3 4 5 6 7 8 9 10 GOOD RUN

NUTRITION

BEFORE	DURING	AFTER

RUN 2

TIME/DISTANCE	WEATHER

COMMENTS

BAD RUN 1 2 3 4 5 6 7 8 9 10 GOOD RUN

NUTRITION

BEFORE	DURING	AFTER

SPEEDWORK

1

TIME/DISTANCE	REPS	RECOVERY

2

TIME/DISTANCE	REPS	RECOVERY

MOOD	LOW	1	2	3	4	5	6	7	8	9	10	HIGH
ENERGY	LOW	1	2	3	4	5	6	7	8	9	10	HIGH
NUTRITION		1	2	3	4	5	6	7	8	9	10	
WATER 8oz		1	2	3	4	5	6	7	8	9	10	

SLEEP DIARY

WEEK 23 SUMMARY

DATE

GOALS MET

GOALS EXCEEDED

NEXT WEEK

RUNNING NOTES

SPEEDWORK NOTES

REFUELING NOTES

	Calories consumed	
MINUS	Calories Used	
EQUALS	Net Calories	
	BMR	
	net calories deficit	

VITAMINS	DOSAGE	QTY

MOOD

1 2 3 4 5 6 7 8 9 10

ENERGY LEVEL

1 2 3 4 5 6 7 8 9 10

Journal

RUN JOURNAL

WEEK 24 | DAY 1 | DATE

RUN

1

TIME/DISTANCE	WEATHER

COMMENTS

BAD RUN 1 2 3 4 5 6 7 8 9 10 GOOD RUN

NUTRITION

BEFORE	DURING	AFTER

RUN

2

TIME/DISTANCE	WEATHER

COMMENTS

BAD RUN 1 2 3 4 5 6 7 8 9 10 GOOD RUN

NUTRITION

BEFORE	DURING	AFTER

SPEEDWORK

1

TIME/DISTANCE	REPS	RECOVERY

2

TIME/DISTANCE	REPS	RECOVERY

MOOD	LOW	1	2	3	4	5	6	7	8	9	10	HIGH
ENERGY	LOW	1	2	3	4	5	6	7	8	9	10	HIGH
NUTRITION		1	2	3	4	5	6	7	8	9	10	
WATER 8oz		1	2	3	4	5	6	7	8	9	10	

SLEEP DIARY

WEEK 24 | DAY 2 | DATE

RUN 1

TIME/DISTANCE	WEATHER

COMMENTS

BAD RUN	1	2	3	4	5	6	7	8	9	10	GOOD RUN

NUTRITION

BEFORE	DURING	AFTER

RUN 2

TIME/DISTANCE	WEATHER

COMMENTS

BAD RUN	1	2	3	4	5	6	7	8	9	10	GOOD RUN

NUTRITION

BEFORE	DURING	AFTER

SPEEDWORK

1

TIME/DISTANCE	REPS	RECOVERY

2

TIME/DISTANCE	REPS	RECOVERY

MOOD	LOW	1	2	3	4	5	6	7	8	9	10	HIGH
ENERGY	LOW	1	2	3	4	5	6	7	8	9	10	HIGH
NUTRITION		1	2	3	4	5	6	7	8	9	10	
WATER 8oz		1	2	3	4	5	6	7	8	9	10	

SLEEP DIARY

RUN JOURNAL

WEEK 24 | DAY 3 | DATE

RUN 1

TIME/DISTANCE | WEATHER

COMMENTS

BAD RUN 1 2 3 4 5 6 7 8 9 10 GOOD RUN

NUTRITION

BEFORE | DURING | AFTER

RUN 2

TIME/DISTANCE | WEATHER

COMMENTS

BAD RUN 1 2 3 4 5 6 7 8 9 10 GOOD RUN

NUTRITION

BEFORE | DURING | AFTER

SPEEDWORK

1

TIME/DISTANCE	REPS	RECOVERY

2

TIME/DISTANCE	REPS	RECOVERY

MOOD	LOW	1	2	3	4	5	6	7	8	9	10	HIGH
ENERGY	LOW	1	2	3	4	5	6	7	8	9	10	HIGH
NUTRITION		1	2	3	4	5	6	7	8	9	10	
WATER 8oz		1	2	3	4	5	6	7	8	9	10	

SLEEP DIARY

WEEK 24 | DAY 4 | DATE

RUN 1

TIME/DISTANCE	WEATHER

COMMENTS

BAD RUN 1 2 3 4 5 6 7 8 9 10 GOOD RUN

NUTRITION

BEFORE	DURING	AFTER

RUN 2

TIME/DISTANCE	WEATHER

COMMENTS

BAD RUN 1 2 3 4 5 6 7 8 9 10 GOOD RUN

NUTRITION

BEFORE	DURING	AFTER

SPEEDWORK

1

TIME/DISTANCE	REPS	RECOVERY

2

TIME/DISTANCE	REPS	RECOVERY

MOOD	LOW	1	2	3	4	5	6	7	8	9	10	HIGH
ENERGY	LOW	1	2	3	4	5	6	7	8	9	10	HIGH
NUTRITION		1	2	3	4	5	6	7	8	9	10	
WATER 8oz		1	2	3	4	5	6	7	8	9	10	

SLEEP DIARY

RUN JOURNAL

WEEK 24 | DAY 5 | DATE

RUN

1

TIME/DISTANCE	WEATHER

COMMENTS

BAD RUN 1 2 3 4 5 6 7 8 9 10 GOOD RUN

NUTRITION

BEFORE	DURING	AFTER

RUN

2

TIME/DISTANCE	WEATHER

COMMENTS

BAD RUN 1 2 3 4 5 6 7 8 9 10 GOOD RUN

NUTRITION

BEFORE	DURING	AFTER

SPEEDWORK

1

TIME/DISTANCE	REPS	RECOVERY

2

TIME/DISTANCE	REPS	RECOVERY

MOOD	LOW	1	2	3	4	5	6	7	8	9	10	HIGH
ENERGY	LOW	1	2	3	4	5	6	7	8	9	10	HIGH
NUTRITION		1	2	3	4	5	6	7	8	9	10	
WATER 8oz		1	2	3	4	5	6	7	8	9	10	

SLEEP DIARY

WEEK 24 | DAY 6 | DATE

RUN 1

TIME/DISTANCE	WEATHER

COMMENTS

BAD RUN 1 2 3 4 5 6 7 8 9 10 GOOD RUN

NUTRITION

BEFORE	DURING	AFTER

RUN 2

TIME/DISTANCE	WEATHER

COMMENTS

BAD RUN 1 2 3 4 5 6 7 8 9 10 GOOD RUN

NUTRITION

BEFORE	DURING	AFTER

SPEEDWORK

1

TIME/DISTANCE	REPS	RECOVERY

2

TIME/DISTANCE	REPS	RECOVERY

MOOD	LOW	1	2	3	4	5	6	7	8	9	10	HIGH
ENERGY	LOW	1	2	3	4	5	6	7	8	9	10	HIGH
NUTRITION		1	2	3	4	5	6	7	8	9	10	
WATER 8oz		1	2	3	4	5	6	7	8	9	10	

SLEEP DIARY

RUN JOURNAL

WEEK 24 | DAY 7 | DATE

RUN

1

TIME/DISTANCE	WEATHER

COMMENTS

BAD RUN	1	2	3	4	5	6	7	8	9	10	GOOD RUN

NUTRITION

BEFORE	DURING	AFTER

RUN

2

TIME/DISTANCE	WEATHER

COMMENTS

BAD RUN	1	2	3	4	5	6	7	8	9	10	GOOD RUN

NUTRITION

BEFORE	DURING	AFTER

SPEEDWORK

1

TIME/DISTANCE	REPS	RECOVERY

2

TIME/DISTANCE	REPS	RECOVERY

MOOD	LOW	1	2	3	4	5	6	7	8	9	10	HIGH
ENERGY	LOW	1	2	3	4	5	6	7	8	9	10	HIGH
NUTRITION		1	2	3	4	5	6	7	8	9	10	
WATER 8oz		1	2	3	4	5	6	7	8	9	10	

SLEEP DIARY

WEEK 24 SUMMARY

DATE

GOALS MET

GOALS EXCEEDED

NEXT WEEK

RUNNING NOTES

SPEEDWORK NOTES

REFUELING NOTES

Calories consumed	
MINUS Calories Used	
EQUALS Net Calories	
BMR	
net calories deficit	

VITAMINS	DOSAGE	QTY

MOOD

1 2 3 4 5 6 7 8 9 10

ENERGY LEVEL

1 2 3 4 5 6 7 8 9 10

Journal

MONTH 6 SUMMARY

GOALS MET | GOALS EXCEEDED | MAYBE NEXT WEEK

RUNNING NOTES

SPEEDWORK NOTES

MOOD & ENERGY

TOTAL RUNNING SESSIONS

TOTAL SPEEDWORK SESSIONS

GOALS FOR NEXT MONTH

RUN TRAINING GOALS	SPEED TRAINING GOALS

NEW SHOES?

It is claimed that new running shoes can knock a few percent of your best time once you have worn them in. Have a good look at your running shoes, how long you have had them?, if it's more than a year the chances are they are not offering much protection or cushioning. When buying new trainers go to a professional running shop where they can look at your running style and how your foot hits the ground when you are running to recommend the best running trainers in your budget.

RUN JOURNAL

WEEK 25 | DAY 1 | DATE

RUN 1

TIME/DISTANCE	WEATHER

COMMENTS

BAD RUN 1 2 3 4 5 6 7 8 9 10 GOOD RUN

NUTRITION

BEFORE	DURING	AFTER

RUN 2

TIME/DISTANCE	WEATHER

COMMENTS

BAD RUN 1 2 3 4 5 6 7 8 9 10 GOOD RUN

NUTRITION

BEFORE	DURING	AFTER

SPEEDWORK

1

TIME/DISTANCE	REPS	RECOVERY

2

TIME/DISTANCE	REPS	RECOVERY

MOOD	LOW	1	2	3	4	5	6	7	8	9	10	HIGH
ENERGY	LOW	1	2	3	4	5	6	7	8	9	10	HIGH
NUTRITION		1	2	3	4	5	6	7	8	9	10	
WATER 8oz		1	2	3	4	5	6	7	8	9	10	

SLEEP DIARY

WEEK 25 | DAY 2 | DATE

RUN 1

TIME/DISTANCE	WEATHER

COMMENTS

BAD RUN	1	2	3	4	5	6	7	8	9	10	GOOD RUN

NUTRITION

BEFORE	DURING	AFTER

RUN 2

TIME/DISTANCE	WEATHER

COMMENTS

BAD RUN	1	2	3	4	5	6	7	8	9	10	GOOD RUN

NUTRITION

BEFORE	DURING	AFTER

SPEEDWORK

1

TIME/DISTANCE	REPS	RECOVERY

2

TIME/DISTANCE	REPS	RECOVERY

MOOD	LOW	1	2	3	4	5	6	7	8	9	10	HIGH
ENERGY	LOW	1	2	3	4	5	6	7	8	9	10	HIGH
NUTRITION		1	2	3	4	5	6	7	8	9	10	
WATER 8oz		1	2	3	4	5	6	7	8	9	10	

SLEEP DIARY

RUN JOURNAL

WEEK 25 | DAY 3 | DATE

RUN

1

TIME/ DISTANCE	WEATHER

COMMENTS

BAD RUN 1 2 3 4 5 6 7 8 9 10 GOOD RUN

NUTRITION

BEFORE	DURING	AFTER

RUN

2

TIME/ DISTANCE	WEATHER

COMMENTS

BAD RUN 1 2 3 4 5 6 7 8 9 10 GOOD RUN

NUTRITION

BEFORE	DURING	AFTER

SPEEDWORK

1

TIME/ DISTANCE	REPS	RECOVERY

2

TIME/ DISTANCE	REPS	RECOVERY

MOOD	LOW 1	2	3	4	5	6	7	8	9	10	HIGH
ENERGY	LOW 1	2	3	4	5	6	7	8	9	10	HIGH
NUTRITION	1	2	3	4	5	6	7	8	9	10	
WATER 8oz	1	2	3	4	5	6	7	8	9	10	

SLEEP DIARY

WEEK 25 | DAY 4 | DATE

RUN 1

TIME/DISTANCE	WEATHER

COMMENTS

BAD RUN 1 2 3 4 5 6 7 8 9 10 GOOD RUN

NUTRITION

BEFORE	DURING	AFTER

RUN 2

TIME/DISTANCE	WEATHER

COMMENTS

BAD RUN 1 2 3 4 5 6 7 8 9 10 GOOD RUN

NUTRITION

BEFORE	DURING	AFTER

SPEEDWORK

1

TIME/DISTANCE	REPS	RECOVERY

2

TIME/DISTANCE	REPS	RECOVERY

MOOD	LOW	1	2	3	4	5	6	7	8	9	10	HIGH
ENERGY	LOW	1	2	3	4	5	6	7	8	9	10	HIGH
NUTRITION		1	2	3	4	5	6	7	8	9	10	
WATER 8oz		1	2	3	4	5	6	7	8	9	10	

SLEEP DIARY

RUN JOURNAL

WEEK 25 | DAY 5 | DATE

RUN 1

TIME/DISTANCE	WEATHER

COMMENTS

BAD RUN 1 2 3 4 5 6 7 8 9 10 GOOD RUN

NUTRITION

BEFORE	DURING	AFTER

RUN 2

TIME/DISTANCE	WEATHER

COMMENTS

BAD RUN 1 2 3 4 5 6 7 8 9 10 GOOD RUN

NUTRITION

BEFORE	DURING	AFTER

SPEEDWORK

1

TIME/DISTANCE	REPS	RECOVERY

2

TIME/DISTANCE	REPS	RECOVERY

MOOD	LOW	1	2	3	4	5	6	7	8	9	10	HIGH
ENERGY	LOW	1	2	3	4	5	6	7	8	9	10	HIGH
NUTRITION		1	2	3	4	5	6	7	8	9	10	
WATER 8oz		1	2	3	4	5	6	7	8	9	10	

SLEEP DIARY

WEEK 25 | DAY 6 | DATE

RUN

1

TIME/DISTANCE	WEATHER

COMMENTS

BAD RUN 1 2 3 4 5 6 7 8 9 10 GOOD RUN

NUTRITION

BEFORE	DURING	AFTER

RUN

2

TIME/DISTANCE	WEATHER

COMMENTS

BAD RUN 1 2 3 4 5 6 7 8 9 10 GOOD RUN

NUTRITION

BEFORE	DURING	AFTER

SPEEDWORK

1

TIME/DISTANCE	REPS	RECOVERY

2

TIME/DISTANCE	REPS	RECOVERY

MOOD	LOW	1	2	3	4	5	6	7	8	9	10	HIGH
ENERGY	LOW	1	2	3	4	5	6	7	8	9	10	HIGH
NUTRITION		1	2	3	4	5	6	7	8	9	10	
WATER 8oz		1	2	3	4	5	6	7	8	9	10	

SLEEP DIARY

RUN JOURNAL

WEEK 25 | DAY 7 | DATE

RUN 1

TIME/DISTANCE	WEATHER

COMMENTS

BAD RUN 1 2 3 4 5 6 7 8 9 10 GOOD RUN

NUTRITION

BEFORE	DURING	AFTER

RUN 2

TIME/DISTANCE	WEATHER

COMMENTS

BAD RUN 1 2 3 4 5 6 7 8 9 10 GOOD RUN

NUTRITION

BEFORE	DURING	AFTER

SPEEDWORK

1

TIME/DISTANCE	REPS	RECOVERY

2

TIME/DISTANCE	REPS	RECOVERY

MOOD	LOW	1	2	3	4	5	6	7	8	9	10	HIGH
ENERGY	LOW	1	2	3	4	5	6	7	8	9	10	HIGH
NUTRITION		1	2	3	4	5	6	7	8	9	10	
WATER 8oz		1	2	3	4	5	6	7	8	9	10	

SLEEP DIARY

WEEK 25 SUMMARY

DATE

GOALS MET

GOALS EXCEEDED

NEXT WEEK

RUNNING NOTES

SPEEDWORK NOTES

REFUELING NOTES

Calories consumed	
MINUS Calories Used	
EQUALS Net Calories	
BMR	
net calories deficit	

VITAMINS	DOSAGE	QTY

MOOD

1 2 3 4 5 6 7 8 9 10

ENERGY LEVEL

1 2 3 4 5 6 7 8 9 10

Journal

RUN JOURNAL

WEEK 26 | DAY 1 | DATE

RUN

1

TIME/DISTANCE	WEATHER

COMMENTS

BAD RUN 1 2 3 4 5 6 7 8 9 10 GOOD RUN

NUTRITION

BEFORE	DURING	AFTER

RUN

2

TIME/DISTANCE	WEATHER

COMMENTS

BAD RUN 1 2 3 4 5 6 7 8 9 10 GOOD RUN

NUTRITION

BEFORE	DURING	AFTER

SPEEDWORK

1

TIME/DISTANCE	REPS	RECOVERY

2

TIME/DISTANCE	REPS	RECOVERY

MOOD	LOW	1	2	3	4	5	6	7	8	9	10	HIGH
ENERGY	LOW	1	2	3	4	5	6	7	8	9	10	HIGH
NUTRITION		1	2	3	4	5	6	7	8	9	10	
WATER 8oz		1	2	3	4	5	6	7	8	9	10	

SLEEP DIARY

WEEK 26 | DAY 2 | DATE

RUN

1

TIME/DISTANCE	WEATHER

COMMENTS

BAD RUN 1 2 3 4 5 6 7 8 9 10 GOOD RUN

NUTRITION

BEFORE	DURING	AFTER

RUN

2

TIME/DISTANCE	WEATHER

COMMENTS

BAD RUN 1 2 3 4 5 6 7 8 9 10 GOOD RUN

NUTRITION

BEFORE	DURING	AFTER

SPEEDWORK

1

TIME/DISTANCE	REPS	RECOVERY

2

TIME/DISTANCE	REPS	RECOVERY

MOOD	LOW	1	2	3	4	5	6	7	8	9	10	HIGH
ENERGY	LOW	1	2	3	4	5	6	7	8	9	10	HIGH
NUTRITION		1	2	3	4	5	6	7	8	9	10	
WATER 8oz		1	2	3	4	5	6	7	8	9	10	

SLEEP DIARY

RUN JOURNAL

WEEK 26	DAY 3	DATE

RUN 1

TIME/DISTANCE	WEATHER

COMMENTS

BAD RUN	1	2	3	4	5	6	7	8	9	10	GOOD RUN

NUTRITION

BEFORE	DURING	AFTER

RUN 2

TIME/DISTANCE	WEATHER

COMMENTS

BAD RUN	1	2	3	4	5	6	7	8	9	10	GOOD RUN

NUTRITION

BEFORE	DURING	AFTER

SPEEDWORK

1

TIME/DISTANCE	REPS	RECOVERY

2

TIME/DISTANCE	REPS	RECOVERY

MOOD	LOW	1	2	3	4	5	6	7	8	9	10	HIGH
ENERGY	LOW	1	2	3	4	5	6	7	8	9	10	HIGH
NUTRITION		1	2	3	4	5	6	7	8	9	10	
WATER 8oz		1	2	3	4	5	6	7	8	9	10	

SLEEP DIARY

WEEK 26 | DAY 4 | DATE

RUN

1

TIME/DISTANCE	WEATHER

COMMENTS

BAD RUN 1 2 3 4 5 6 7 8 9 10 GOOD RUN

NUTRITION

BEFORE	DURING	AFTER

RUN

2

TIME/DISTANCE	WEATHER

COMMENTS

BAD RUN 1 2 3 4 5 6 7 8 9 10 GOOD RUN

NUTRITION

BEFORE	DURING	AFTER

SPEEDWORK

1

TIME/DISTANCE	REPS	RECOVERY

2

TIME/DISTANCE	REPS	RECOVERY

MOOD	LOW	1	2	3	4	5	6	7	8	9	10	HIGH
ENERGY	LOW	1	2	3	4	5	6	7	8	9	10	HIGH
NUTRITION		1	2	3	4	5	6	7	8	9	10	
WATER 8oz		1	2	3	4	5	6	7	8	9	10	

SLEEP DIARY

RUN JOURNAL

WEEK 26 | DAY 5 | DATE

RUN 1

TIME/DISTANCE	WEATHER

COMMENTS

BAD RUN 1 2 3 4 5 6 7 8 9 10 GOOD RUN

NUTRITION

BEFORE	DURING	AFTER

RUN 2

TIME/DISTANCE	WEATHER

COMMENTS

BAD RUN 1 2 3 4 5 6 7 8 9 10 GOOD RUN

NUTRITION

BEFORE	DURING	AFTER

SPEEDWORK

1

TIME/DISTANCE	REPS	RECOVERY

2

TIME/DISTANCE	REPS	RECOVERY

MOOD	LOW	1	2	3	4	5	6	7	8	9	10	HIGH
ENERGY	LOW	1	2	3	4	5	6	7	8	9	10	HIGH
NUTRITION		1	2	3	4	5	6	7	8	9	10	
WATER 8oz		1	2	3	4	5	6	7	8	9	10	

SLEEP DIARY

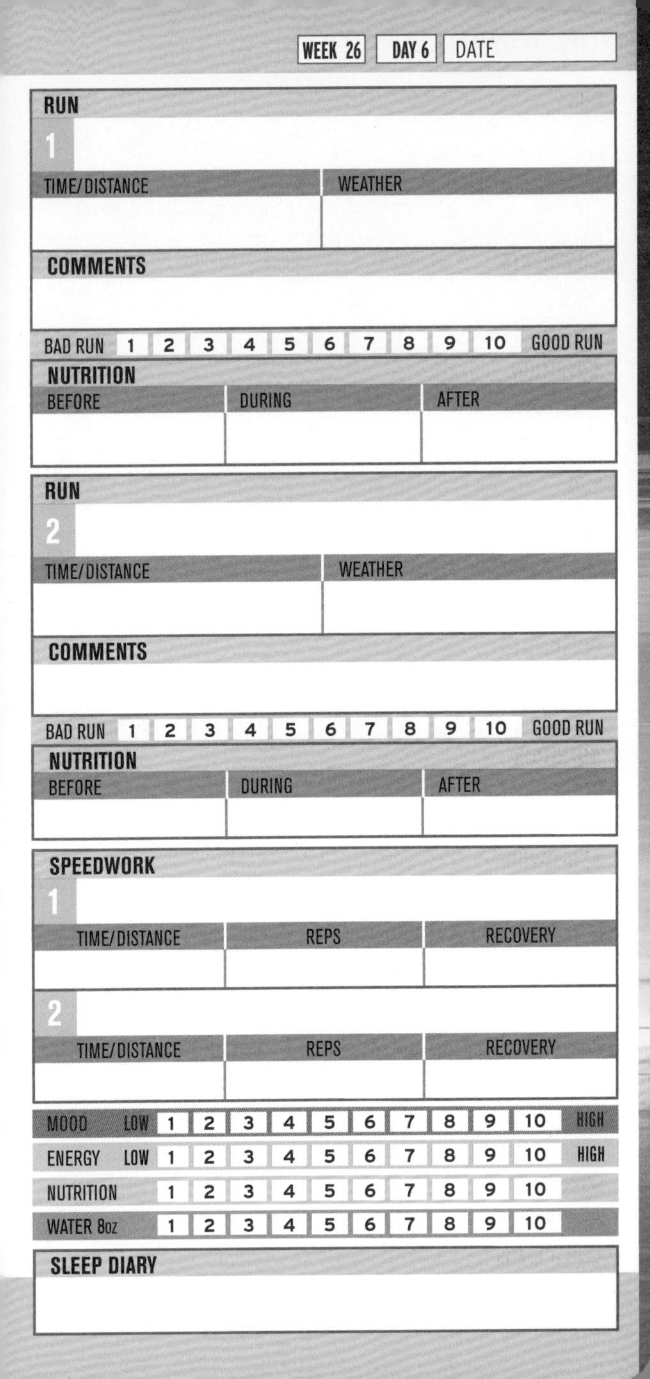

WEEK 26 | DAY 6 | DATE

RUN

1

TIME/DISTANCE	WEATHER

COMMENTS

BAD RUN 1 2 3 4 5 6 7 8 9 10 GOOD RUN

NUTRITION

BEFORE	DURING	AFTER

RUN

2

TIME/DISTANCE	WEATHER

COMMENTS

BAD RUN 1 2 3 4 5 6 7 8 9 10 GOOD RUN

NUTRITION

BEFORE	DURING	AFTER

SPEEDWORK

1

TIME/DISTANCE	REPS	RECOVERY

2

TIME/DISTANCE	REPS	RECOVERY

MOOD	LOW	1	2	3	4	5	6	7	8	9	10	HIGH
ENERGY	LOW	1	2	3	4	5	6	7	8	9	10	HIGH
NUTRITION		1	2	3	4	5	6	7	8	9	10	
WATER 8oz		1	2	3	4	5	6	7	8	9	10	

SLEEP DIARY

RUN JOURNAL

WEEK 26 | DAY 7 | DATE

RUN 1

TIME/DISTANCE	WEATHER

COMMENTS

BAD RUN 1 2 3 4 5 6 7 8 9 10 GOOD RUN

NUTRITION

BEFORE	DURING	AFTER

RUN 2

TIME/DISTANCE	WEATHER

COMMENTS

BAD RUN 1 2 3 4 5 6 7 8 9 10 GOOD RUN

NUTRITION

BEFORE	DURING	AFTER

SPEEDWORK

1

TIME/DISTANCE	REPS	RECOVERY

2

TIME/DISTANCE	REPS	RECOVERY

MOOD	LOW	1	2	3	4	5	6	7	8	9	10	HIGH
ENERGY	LOW	1	2	3	4	5	6	7	8	9	10	HIGH
NUTRITION		1	2	3	4	5	6	7	8	9	10	
WATER 8oz		1	2	3	4	5	6	7	8	9	10	

SLEEP DIARY

WEEK 26 SUMMARY

DATE

GOALS MET

GOALS EXCEEDED

NEXT WEEK

RUNNING NOTES

SPEEDWORK NOTES

REFUELING NOTES

Calories consumed	
MINUS Calories Used	
EQUALS Net Calories	
BMR	
net calories deficit	

VITAMINS	DOSAGE	QTY

MOOD

1 2 3 4 5 6 7 8 9 10

ENERGY LEVEL

1 2 3 4 5 6 7 8 9 10

Journal

RUN JOURNAL

WEEK 27 | DAY 1 | DATE

RUN 1

TIME/DISTANCE | WEATHER

COMMENTS

BAD RUN 1 2 3 4 5 6 7 8 9 10 GOOD RUN

NUTRITION

BEFORE | DURING | AFTER

RUN 2

TIME/DISTANCE | WEATHER

COMMENTS

BAD RUN 1 2 3 4 5 6 7 8 9 10 GOOD RUN

NUTRITION

BEFORE | DURING | AFTER

SPEEDWORK

1

TIME/DISTANCE	REPS	RECOVERY

2

TIME/DISTANCE	REPS	RECOVERY

MOOD	LOW	1	2	3	4	5	6	7	8	9	10	HIGH
ENERGY	LOW	1	2	3	4	5	6	7	8	9	10	HIGH
NUTRITION		1	2	3	4	5	6	7	8	9	10	
WATER 8oz		1	2	3	4	5	6	7	8	9	10	

SLEEP DIARY

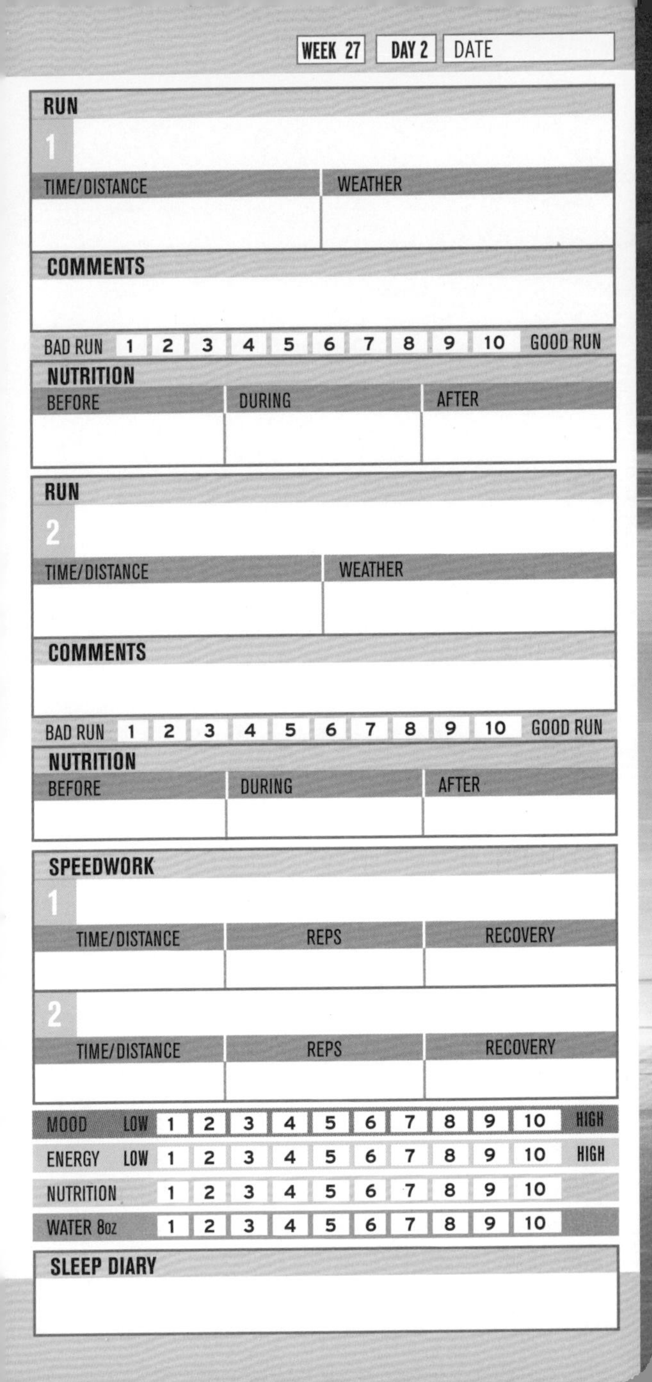

WEEK 27 | DAY 2 | DATE

RUN

1

TIME/DISTANCE	WEATHER

COMMENTS

BAD RUN 1 2 3 4 5 6 7 8 9 10 GOOD RUN

NUTRITION

BEFORE	DURING	AFTER

RUN

2

TIME/DISTANCE	WEATHER

COMMENTS

BAD RUN 1 2 3 4 5 6 7 8 9 10 GOOD RUN

NUTRITION

BEFORE	DURING	AFTER

SPEEDWORK

1

TIME/DISTANCE	REPS	RECOVERY

2

TIME/DISTANCE	REPS	RECOVERY

MOOD	LOW	1	2	3	4	5	6	7	8	9	10	HIGH
ENERGY	LOW	1	2	3	4	5	6	7	8	9	10	HIGH
NUTRITION		1	2	3	4	5	6	7	8	9	10	
WATER 8oz		1	2	3	4	5	6	7	8	9	10	

SLEEP DIARY

RUN JOURNAL

WEEK 27 | DAY 3 | DATE

RUN

1

TIME/DISTANCE	WEATHER

COMMENTS

BAD RUN 1 2 3 4 5 6 7 8 9 10 GOOD RUN

NUTRITION

BEFORE	DURING	AFTER

RUN

2

TIME/DISTANCE	WEATHER

COMMENTS

BAD RUN 1 2 3 4 5 6 7 8 9 10 GOOD RUN

NUTRITION

BEFORE	DURING	AFTER

SPEEDWORK

1

TIME/DISTANCE	REPS	RECOVERY

2

TIME/DISTANCE	REPS	RECOVERY

MOOD	LOW	1	2	3	4	5	6	7	8	9	10	HIGH
ENERGY	LOW	1	2	3	4	5	6	7	8	9	10	HIGH
NUTRITION		1	2	3	4	5	6	7	8	9	10	
WATER 8oz		1	2	3	4	5	6	7	8	9	10	

SLEEP DIARY

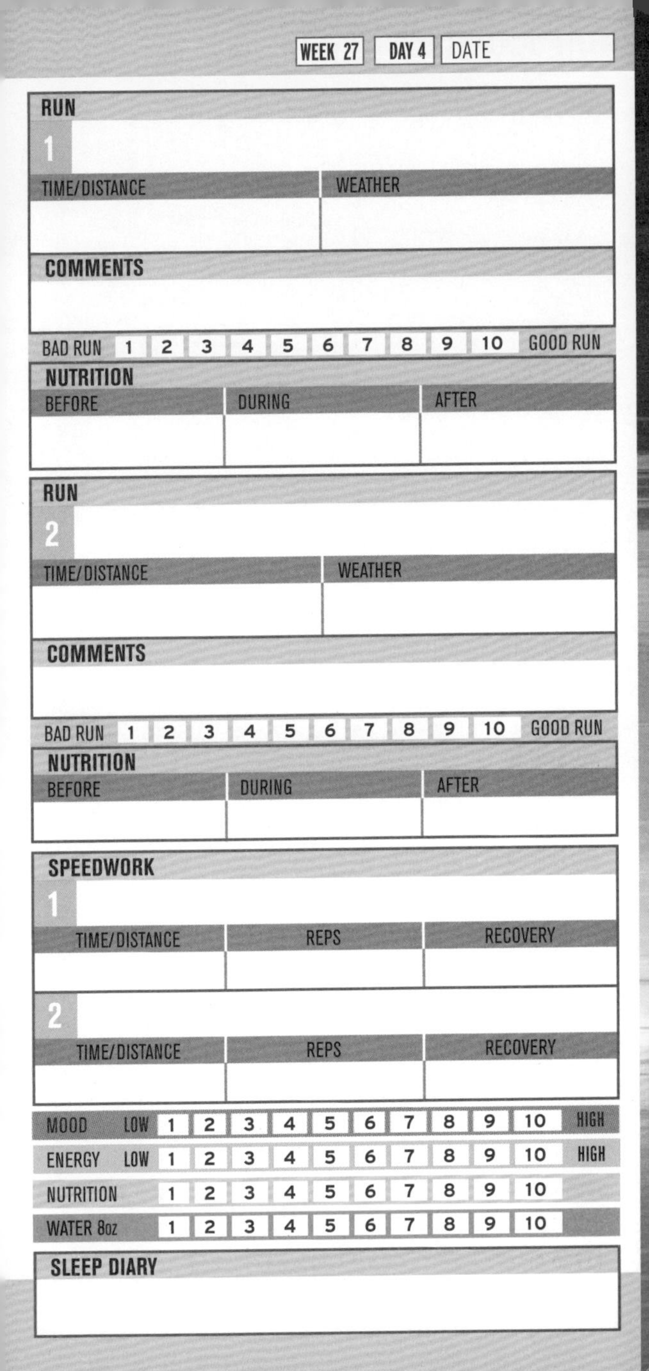
WEEK 27
DAY 4
DATE
RUN
1
TIME/DISTANCE
WEATHER
COMMENTS
BAD RUN 1 2 3 4 5 6 7 8 9 10 GOOD RUN
NUTRITION
BEFORE
DURING
AFTER
RUN
2
TIME/DISTANCE
WEATHER
COMMENTS
BAD RUN 1 2 3 4 5 6 7 8 9 10 GOOD RUN
NUTRITION
BEFORE
DURING
AFTER
SPEEDWORK
1
TIME/DISTANCE
REPS
RECOVERY
2
TIME/DISTANCE
REPS
RECOVERY
MOOD LOW 1 2 3 4 5 6 7 8 9 10 HIGH
ENERGY LOW 1 2 3 4 5 6 7 8 9 10 HIGH
NUTRITION 1 2 3 4 5 6 7 8 9 10
WATER 8oz 1 2 3 4 5 6 7 8 9 10
SLEEP DIARY

RUN JOURNAL

WEEK 27 | DAY 5 | DATE

RUN 1

TIME/DISTANCE	WEATHER

COMMENTS

BAD RUN 1 2 3 4 5 6 7 8 9 10 GOOD RUN

NUTRITION

BEFORE	DURING	AFTER

RUN 2

TIME/DISTANCE	WEATHER

COMMENTS

BAD RUN 1 2 3 4 5 6 7 8 9 10 GOOD RUN

NUTRITION

BEFORE	DURING	AFTER

SPEEDWORK

1

TIME/DISTANCE	REPS	RECOVERY

2

TIME/DISTANCE	REPS	RECOVERY

MOOD	LOW	1	2	3	4	5	6	7	8	9	10	HIGH
ENERGY	LOW	1	2	3	4	5	6	7	8	9	10	HIGH
NUTRITION		1	2	3	4	5	6	7	8	9	10	
WATER 8oz		1	2	3	4	5	6	7	8	9	10	

SLEEP DIARY

WEEK 27 | DAY 6 | DATE

RUN 1

TIME/DISTANCE	WEATHER

COMMENTS

BAD RUN 1 2 3 4 5 6 7 8 9 10 GOOD RUN

NUTRITION

BEFORE	DURING	AFTER

RUN 2

TIME/DISTANCE	WEATHER

COMMENTS

BAD RUN 1 2 3 4 5 6 7 8 9 10 GOOD RUN

NUTRITION

BEFORE	DURING	AFTER

SPEEDWORK

1

TIME/DISTANCE	REPS	RECOVERY

2

TIME/DISTANCE	REPS	RECOVERY

MOOD	LOW	1	2	3	4	5	6	7	8	9	10	HIGH
ENERGY	LOW	1	2	3	4	5	6	7	8	9	10	HIGH
NUTRITION		1	2	3	4	5	6	7	8	9	10	
WATER 8oz		1	2	3	4	5	6	7	8	9	10	

SLEEP DIARY

RUN JOURNAL

WEEK 27 | DAY 7 | DATE

RUN 1

TIME/DISTANCE	WEATHER

COMMENTS

BAD RUN 1 2 3 4 5 6 7 8 9 10 GOOD RUN

NUTRITION

BEFORE	DURING	AFTER

RUN 2

TIME/DISTANCE	WEATHER

COMMENTS

BAD RUN 1 2 3 4 5 6 7 8 9 10 GOOD RUN

NUTRITION

BEFORE	DURING	AFTER

SPEEDWORK

1

TIME/DISTANCE	REPS	RECOVERY

2

TIME/DISTANCE	REPS	RECOVERY

MOOD	LOW	1	2	3	4	5	6	7	8	9	10	HIGH
ENERGY	LOW	1	2	3	4	5	6	7	8	9	10	HIGH
NUTRITION		1	2	3	4	5	6	7	8	9	10	
WATER 8oz		1	2	3	4	5	6	7	8	9	10	

SLEEP DIARY

WEEK 27 SUMMARY

DATE

GOALS MET

GOALS EXCEEDED

NEXT WEEK

RUNNING NOTES

SPEEDWORK NOTES

REFUELING NOTES

	Calories consumed	
MINUS	Calories Used	
EQUALS	Net Calories	
	BMR	
	net calories deficit	

VITAMINS	DOSAGE	QTY

MOOD

1 2 3 4 5 6 7 8 9 10

ENERGY LEVEL

1 2 3 4 5 6 7 8 9 10

Journal

RUN JOURNAL

WEEK 28 | DAY 1 | DATE

RUN 1

TIME/DISTANCE	WEATHER

COMMENTS

BAD RUN 1 2 3 4 5 6 7 8 9 10 GOOD RUN

NUTRITION

BEFORE	DURING	AFTER

RUN 2

TIME/DISTANCE	WEATHER

COMMENTS

BAD RUN 1 2 3 4 5 6 7 8 9 10 GOOD RUN

NUTRITION

BEFORE	DURING	AFTER

SPEEDWORK

1

TIME/DISTANCE	REPS	RECOVERY

2

TIME/DISTANCE	REPS	RECOVERY

MOOD	LOW	1	2	3	4	5	6	7	8	9	10	HIGH
ENERGY	LOW	1	2	3	4	5	6	7	8	9	10	HIGH
NUTRITION		1	2	3	4	5	6	7	8	9	10	
WATER 8oz		1	2	3	4	5	6	7	8	9	10	

SLEEP DIARY

WEEK 28 | DAY 2 | DATE

RUN 1

TIME/DISTANCE	WEATHER

COMMENTS

BAD RUN 1 2 3 4 5 6 7 8 9 10 GOOD RUN

NUTRITION

BEFORE	DURING	AFTER

RUN 2

TIME/DISTANCE	WEATHER

COMMENTS

BAD RUN 1 2 3 4 5 6 7 8 9 10 GOOD RUN

NUTRITION

BEFORE	DURING	AFTER

SPEEDWORK

1

TIME/DISTANCE	REPS	RECOVERY

2

TIME/DISTANCE	REPS	RECOVERY

MOOD	LOW	1	2	3	4	5	6	7	8	9	10	HIGH
ENERGY	LOW	1	2	3	4	5	6	7	8	9	10	HIGH
NUTRITION		1	2	3	4	5	6	7	8	9	10	
WATER 8oz		1	2	3	4	5	6	7	8	9	10	

SLEEP DIARY

RUN JOURNAL

WEEK 28 | DAY 3 | DATE

RUN 1

TIME/DISTANCE	WEATHER

COMMENTS

BAD RUN 1 2 3 4 5 6 7 8 9 10 GOOD RUN

NUTRITION

BEFORE	DURING	AFTER

RUN 2

TIME/DISTANCE	WEATHER

COMMENTS

BAD RUN 1 2 3 4 5 6 7 8 9 10 GOOD RUN

NUTRITION

BEFORE	DURING	AFTER

SPEEDWORK

1

TIME/DISTANCE	REPS	RECOVERY

2

TIME/DISTANCE	REPS	RECOVERY

MOOD	LOW	1	2	3	4	5	6	7	8	9	10	HIGH
ENERGY	LOW	1	2	3	4	5	6	7	8	9	10	HIGH
NUTRITION		1	2	3	4	5	6	7	8	9	10	
WATER 8oz		1	2	3	4	5	6	7	8	9	10	

SLEEP DIARY

WEEK 28 | DAY 4 | DATE

RUN 1

TIME/DISTANCE	WEATHER

COMMENTS

BAD RUN 1 2 3 4 5 6 7 8 9 10 GOOD RUN

NUTRITION

BEFORE	DURING	AFTER

RUN 2

TIME/DISTANCE	WEATHER

COMMENTS

BAD RUN 1 2 3 4 5 6 7 8 9 10 GOOD RUN

NUTRITION

BEFORE	DURING	AFTER

SPEEDWORK

1

TIME/DISTANCE	REPS	RECOVERY

2

TIME/DISTANCE	REPS	RECOVERY

MOOD	LOW	1	2	3	4	5	6	7	8	9	10	HIGH
ENERGY	LOW	1	2	3	4	5	6	7	8	9	10	HIGH
NUTRITION		1	2	3	4	5	6	7	8	9	10	
WATER 8oz		1	2	3	4	5	6	7	8	9	10	

SLEEP DIARY

RUN JOURNAL

WEEK 28 | DAY 5 | DATE

RUN 1

TIME/DISTANCE	WEATHER

COMMENTS

BAD RUN 1 2 3 4 5 6 7 8 9 10 GOOD RUN

NUTRITION

BEFORE	DURING	AFTER

RUN 2

TIME/DISTANCE	WEATHER

COMMENTS

BAD RUN 1 2 3 4 5 6 7 8 9 10 GOOD RUN

NUTRITION

BEFORE	DURING	AFTER

SPEEDWORK

1

TIME/DISTANCE	REPS	RECOVERY

2

TIME/DISTANCE	REPS	RECOVERY

MOOD	LOW	1	2	3	4	5	6	7	8	9	10	HIGH
ENERGY	LOW	1	2	3	4	5	6	7	8	9	10	HIGH
NUTRITION		1	2	3	4	5	6	7	8	9	10	
WATER 8oz		1	2	3	4	5	6	7	8	9	10	

SLEEP DIARY

RUN

1

TIME/DISTANCE	WEATHER

COMMENTS

BAD RUN 1 2 3 4 5 6 7 8 9 10 GOOD RUN

NUTRITION

BEFORE	DURING	AFTER

RUN

2

TIME/DISTANCE	WEATHER

COMMENTS

BAD RUN 1 2 3 4 5 6 7 8 9 10 GOOD RUN

NUTRITION

BEFORE	DURING	AFTER

SPEEDWORK

1

TIME/DISTANCE	REPS	RECOVERY

2

TIME/DISTANCE	REPS	RECOVERY

MOOD	LOW	1	2	3	4	5	6	7	8	9	10	HIGH
ENERGY	LOW	1	2	3	4	5	6	7	8	9	10	HIGH
NUTRITION		1	2	3	4	5	6	7	8	9	10	
WATER 8oz		1	2	3	4	5	6	7	8	9	10	

SLEEP DIARY

RUN JOURNAL

WEEK 28 | DAY 7 | DATE

RUN 1

TIME/DISTANCE	WEATHER

COMMENTS

BAD RUN	1	2	3	4	5	6	7	8	9	10	GOOD RUN

NUTRITION

BEFORE	DURING	AFTER

RUN 2

TIME/DISTANCE	WEATHER

COMMENTS

BAD RUN	1	2	3	4	5	6	7	8	9	10	GOOD RUN

NUTRITION

BEFORE	DURING	AFTER

SPEEDWORK

1

TIME/DISTANCE	REPS	RECOVERY

2

TIME/DISTANCE	REPS	RECOVERY

MOOD	LOW	1	2	3	4	5	6	7	8	9	10	HIGH
ENERGY	LOW	1	2	3	4	5	6	7	8	9	10	HIGH
NUTRITION		1	2	3	4	5	6	7	8	9	10	
WATER 8oz		1	2	3	4	5	6	7	8	9	10	

SLEEP DIARY

WEEK 28 SUMMARY

DATE

GOALS MET

GOALS EXCEEDED

NEXT WEEK

RUNNING NOTES

SPEEDWORK NOTES

REFUELING NOTES

Calories consumed	
MINUS Calories Used	
EQUALS Net Calories	
BMR	
net calories deficit	

VITAMINS	DOSAGE	QTY

MOOD

1 2 3 4 5 6 7 8 9 10

ENERGY LEVEL

1 2 3 4 5 6 7 8 9 10

Journal

MONTH 7 SUMMARY

GOALS MET | GOALS EXCEEDED | MAYBE NEXT WEEK

RUNNING NOTES

SPEEDWORK NOTES

MOOD & ENERGY

TOTAL RUNNING SESSIONS

TOTAL SPEEDWORK SESSIONS

GOALS FOR NEXT MONTH

RUN TRAINING GOALS	SPEED TRAINING GOALS

COUNTING TIME

If you want to run a fast marathon or 10k race, you first have to learn how to judge your speed and maintain consistency. Some elite athletes know by the way their foot strikes the ground how fast they are running and will hit that mile marker at the time they want with three to four seconds either side. Start by running three eight-minute miles in a week. The next week try to beat that. If you do this you'll get quicker, and over a period of time you will learn to work out your speed.

COMPETITION/RACE LOG

DATE	EVENT	PLACE	TIME
COMMENTS			

DATE	EVENT	PLACE	TIME
COMMENTS			

DATE	EVENT	PLACE	TIME
COMMENTS			

DATE	EVENT	PLACE	TIME
COMMENTS			

DATE	EVENT	PLACE	TIME
COMMENTS			

DATE	EVENT	PLACE	TIME

COMMENTS

DATE	EVENT	PLACE	TIME

COMMENTS

DATE	EVENT	PLACE	TIME

COMMENTS

DATE	EVENT	PLACE	TIME

COMMENTS

DATE	EVENT	PLACE	TIME

COMMENTS

COMPETITION/RACE LOG

DATE	EVENT	PLACE	TIME
COMMENTS			

DATE	EVENT	PLACE	TIME
COMMENTS			

DATE	EVENT	PLACE	TIME
COMMENTS			

DATE	EVENT	PLACE	TIME
COMMENTS			

DATE	EVENT	PLACE	TIME
COMMENTS			